D1442864

STUDIES IN MODERN ANALYSIS

Studies in Mathematics

The Mathematical Association of America

E. E. Floyd, editor

E. J. McShane
University of Virginia

M. H. Stone
University of Chicago

Edgar R. Lorch
Barnard College, Columbia University

Casper Goffman
Purdue University

Studies in Mathematics

Volume 1

STUDIES IN MODERN ANALYSIS

R. C. Buck, editor
University of Wisconsin

Published by
The Mathematical Association of America

Distributed by
Prentice-Hall, Inc.

Printed in the United States of America
by The Maple Press, Inc., York, Pa.
Prentice-Hall, Inc., Englewood Cliffs, N.J.
54130C

PREFACE

With the appearance of this volume, the Mathematical Association of America has embarked upon a new publishing venture. The MAA Studies in Mathematics will bring to the members of the Association, and to the general mathematical community, expository articles at the collegiate and graduate level on recent developments in mathematics and the teaching of mathematics. We hope that these will help to overcome the communication barrier which has arisen as a natural consequence of the tremendous acceleration in mathematical development that has taken place, especially within the last twenty-five years.

We hope that these volumes of short papers will be used as a basis for seminars, reports, informal talks, and as supplementary material to provide background knowledge for both students and faculty. The range of topics will cover primarily the upper class and beginning graduate years; the volumes that are planned at present will have articles at different levels of difficulty, so that the spectrum of each volume is wide.

The need for expository articles of this nature has been long recognized. Indeed, the MAA set a precedent with its highly successful "What Is ——?" series that first appeared in the *Monthly* more than twenty years ago. Three years ago, Professor

Richard V. Andree of the University of Oklahoma conceived of the plan to reprint these articles in a single volume; it at once became clear that many would have to be rewritten to bring them up to date, while at the same time there were many fields of mathematics that were inadequately represented in the original collection. Taking this as a personal challenge, Andree approached a large segment of the mathematical community; succeeding where others failed, he managed to overcome the natural lethargy of research mathematicians, and amassed an outstanding collection of expository articles. These will form the core of the first few volumes of the Studies. We hope that the momentum which Andree has given this effort will not die, and that the present atmosphere, favorable to expository writing, will persist.

R. P. Dilworth
Chairman, Committee on Publications,
Mathematical Association of America

CONTENTS

INTRODUCTION

R. C. Buck

The four papers that are presented in this volume do not pretend to cover all of modern analysis. They are, however, representative; each discusses topics that are fundamental, both for pure and for applied analysis, and which indeed should be part of the experience of every practicing mathematician, regardless of his field. These papers also achieve something which seems more important to me, for they succeed in the more difficult task of conveying some of the *attitudes* that are characteristic of modern mathematicians.

It would be difficult to devise a concise definition of analysis that is broad enough to cover all that now carries this label. It would seem no longer appropriate to confine analysis to "the theory of functions" since algebra and topology have equal rights to claim this as their domain; indeed, algebra has been called the study of homomorphisms, and topology the study of continuous mappings. The dissolution of traditional boundaries between branches of mathematics is probably the most striking aspect of the modern period of development. In the field of analysis, this has shown itself in a growing concern for matters of

1

structure, and the emergence of what can only be called *algebraic analysis* and *topological analysis*.

These trends are clearly visible in the selections that comprise this volume. In the papers by Stone and Goffman, the algebraic component is apparent. In looking at a continuous function, one remains conscious of the fact that it is at the same time a member of a class of functions forming a mathematical entity such as a linear space or an algebra. Alongside this, we cannot ignore the realization that topological ideas lie at the heart of the fundamental processes of analysis; this is indeed the theme of the paper by McShane, but it is implicit in that of Lorch as well. A modern research paper on partial differential equations may refer to "the compact-open topology," or to the equivalence of "the strong and weak topology"; a paper on function theory may speak of compact sets rather than normal families, and may indeed discuss the nature of closed ideals in an algebra of holomorphic functions.

This intermarriage of traditional analysis with its neighbors has not come about as a rational decision of its practitioners. At first sight, the change seemed to have been largely a matter of semantics; one adopted the terminology of algebra and topology solely as a convenience to describe briefly certain situations which arose frequently. But it soon became evident that the adoption of another viewpoint, another observation platform, gave a clearer vision; the introduction of techniques borrowed from other fields enabled the analyst to achieve both striking economies in proof, and vivid insights into classical phenomena. Two prime examples are included in these papers: the first is the treatment of the Weierstrass approximation theorem, as given in the paper by M. H. Stone; the second, included in the paper by Goffman, is the unified treatment of certain existence theorems that is made possible by the study of contraction mappings on complete metric spaces. An even more persuasive example, not included here, would be the chain of observations that start from the classical theorems of Green and Stokes and culminate in the connection between differential forms and cohomology theory.

Nor is this the only type of contribution that algebra and topology have made to analysis. It is, of course, a platitude to say that they have suggested new problems in analysis. A traditionalist might indeed agree that the query: "What are all the ideals in the ring of entire functions?" is admittedly a new problem for analysis, but express great disinterest in its solution. Similarly, I am sure that a fifteenth-century algebraist would have expressed an equal disdain to someone who asked about the possible nature of the set of values of a polynomial

$$w = P(z) = z + a_2 z^2 + \cdots + a_m z^m,$$

for all z with $|z| < 1$. What is perhaps more convincing to a sceptic is the fact that the insights supplied by new points of view have revived interest in older classical problems, showing them to be the starting point for new attacks on fundamental questions. This has been the case recently with the problem of interpolation by bounded analytic functions, and the problem of equivalence of measure-preserving transformations.

Another theme of modern analysis that is illustrated in detail by the brilliant paper by Lorch is the role of the "abstract" approach in linear analysis. No one would deny that it is convenient to make use of a properly chosen basis at some stage in the study of a particular linear transformation. But it is almost always advantageous to postpone this step as long as possible. This is most evident when one turns to linear operators on Hilbert space; here, the use of matrices, indices, and summations becomes tedious, distracting and, indeed, misleading. Moreover, every problem seems to have its own natural basis, its own ideal set of coordinates, which is seldom the one initially given; it therefore pays to begin by looking at the space abstractly, unprejudiced by irrelevant bias.

A word or two about the specific contents of each of the papers may be in order. The lead-off paper by McShane focuses on the notion of convergence. Certainly, the idea of limit and sequence is basic to elementary calculus. However, one mark of modern analysis has been its concern with more general notions of limit, and with nonmetric topologies and phenomena that escape the restriction imposed by sequences. For example, consider the topology on functions described as "pointwise convergence."

This is nonmetrizable; if $\mathfrak{F}$ is the class of continuous functions f with $0 \leq f(x) \leq 2$ for $0 \leq x \leq 1$ and such that

$$\int_0^1 f(x) \, dx = 1,$$

then the function 2 is in the closure of $\mathfrak{F}$, although (by the Lebesgue convergence theorem) it is not the limit of any *sequence* of functions in $\mathfrak{F}$. The importance of these ideas was seen independently by E. H. Moore and M. Picone, and developed by H. L. Smith, H. Cartan, and others, emerging as a sophisticated tool formulated in terms of "nets," "directed systems," or "filters." In the present paper, McShane has given an extremely lucid introduction to these ideas, using the notion of a "direction" as the unifying principle. With many examples, he shows how a single concept of limit can be used to discuss convergence of functions, sequences, Riemann sums, and more general objects. This paper can be read by any student who has completed elementary calculus and is prepared to re-examine the notion of limit.

The second paper in the volume is reprinted, with minor changes, from the *Mathematics Magazine*. It is a justly famous paper, honored by being probably the most frequently cited research paper in history. In its original form, it is virtually unavailable; these facts alone would justify its inclusion in this volume. However, the Stone-Weierstrass theorem, as the contents of the paper have come to be known, represents one of the first and most striking examples of the success of the algebraic approach to analysis. There are many briefer proofs of the classical Weierstrass approximation theorem in the literature, but no other presentation approaches this one in its richness of insight, depth of application, and variety of structure. The subject of study is the space $\mathfrak{F}$ of continuous real-valued functions on a compact space S; the central problem is to characterize the functions that are uniform limits of functions generated from a subset $\mathfrak{F}_0$ by means of certain specified algebraic operations. In turn, Stone allows first the lattice operations max and min, then these together with addition, and finally addition and

multiplication alone. In each case, the result is used to charac-
terize the appropriate closed ideals in $\mathfrak{F}$. By specializing S and $\mathfrak{F}_0$,
Stone then obtains a wide variety of interesting applications,
ranging from the Tietze-Lebesgue-Urysohn extension theorem
and a theorem of Dieudonné on approximation of functions of
infinitely many variables, to the Peter-Weyl theorem on group
representations. More unusual, perhaps, are the sections dealing
with approximation on $[0, \infty)$ and $(-\infty, \infty)$, related to the
study of Laguerre and Hermite polynomials. Although this paper
calls for a greater mathematical sophistication than is common
with undergraduates, I cannot think of a better introduction to
the spirit of modern mathematics.

Turning now to the third paper, Lorch has managed, in a
comparatively brief span, to give a lucid and even anecdotal
account of the historical development of the spectral theorem.
Starting with the three-dimensional case and a linear transformation H, he asks: "Is there a basis for the space in which the matrix
for H becomes especially simple?" Motivating each transition
point, the reader is led through the analysis of this case, the formulation of the general problem for symmetric operators H on Hilbert
space, the nature of the solution when H is completely continuous, and the new phenomena that arise when H is allowed
to be merely continuous. Finally, omitting details of the proofs
but presenting the ideas convincingly, Lorch outlines a treatment of the unbounded (self-adjoint) case based upon the
von Neumann approach.

The great breadth of subject-matter within modern analysis is
illustrated by the fact that the concluding paper by Goffman,
written independently of that by Lorch and in the same general
area, has remarkably little overlap. Functional analysis—and
indeed, the idea of abstract spaces themselves—seems to have
arisen at the close of the nineteenth century. Initiated and
encouraged by E. H. Moore and Volterra, the stimulus came in
part from the study of the calculus of variations, and from recent
discoveries in differential and integral equations. It is with this
background that the paper by Goffman opens. Many fundamental results in classical analysis can be transcribed to assert

that some continuous transformation T on a space of functions has a fixed point f_0, with $T(f_0) = f_0$; it is natural to attempt to find f_0 by examining the sequence of iterates $T^n g$, for some initial guess g. This leads in turn to the study of distance-decreasing mappings on metric spaces, and the exploration of the notion of compactness in function spaces. This again proves its usefulness when one tries to minimize a (lower semi) continuous function on an appropriate function space (space of curves, in the older terminology of Volterra). Leaving the metric case, Goffman turns to Banach and Hilbert spaces and discusses the role of normed algebras, proving in particular the Gelfand theorem on normed fields, and concluding with the algebraic proof of the theorem by Wiener on absolutely convergent Fourier series.

These articles are not intended as texts; they have more the role of commentaries, of annotated guide books to the mathematical literature. They do not attempt to bring one up to the level of current research. Their aim is preparatory, to pave the way for the more complete story that is yet to come.

They were not written for the expert; perhaps for this reason, experts will enjoy them.

A THEORY OF LIMITS

E. J. McShane

1. INTRODUCTION

One of the distinctive features of twentieth-century mathematics is its seeking for unification and generality. When two or more mathematical theories show strong resemblances, it is almost a conditioned reflex for the modern mathematician to look for the underlying common properties that cause the similarities and to construct a general theory on the basis of those common properties. The theory of limits is a good example. During the nineteenth century many limit processes were defined that led to similar theorems. In 1922 E. H. Moore and H. L. Smith† published a general theory containing the earlier theories as special cases. The fundamental theorems on limits,

---

† E. H. Moore and H. L. Smith, "A general theory of limits," *American Journal of Mathematics*, vol. 44, 1922, p. 102. The same theory was devised independently by M. Picone ("Lezioni di analisi infinitesimale," *Circolo matematico di Catania*, 1923).

once proved in the general setting, could be used in all the special cases without having to be proved over and over.

In this section we shall investigate a general theory of limits that is a modification of the Moore-Smith theory; I believe that the modifications make it somewhat easier to grasp and to use.

2. NOTATION

We shall use the idea of sets and a few of the simplest relations between sets; in fact, the only symbols from set theory that we shall use are $A \subset B$ ("A is contained in B"), meaning that each member of A belongs to B; $A \cap B$ ("the intersection of A and B"), meaning the set of all things that are members of A and also are members of B; and $A \cup B$ ("the union of A and B"), meaning the set of all things belonging to A, or to B, or to both of them. Our chief interest will be in real-valued functions. But since infinite limits are too useful to reject, we augment the real number system R by adjoining two new objects, $+\infty$ and $-\infty$, and we order them by setting $-\infty < a < \infty$ for all real a. The augmented system we call the *extended real number system*, and we denote it by R^*. Since we are going to allow limits in R^*, we may as well allow functional values in R^* too.

If a and b are in R^* and $a < b$, we define the *open interval* (a, b) to be the set of all x in R^* such that $a < x < b$. Likewise, we define the *half-open intervals* $(a, b]$ and $[a, b)$ to be the sets of all x in R^* satisfying the condition $a < x \leq b$ or $a \leq x < b$, respectively. Also, if $a \leq b$, the *closed interval* $[a, b]$ is the set of all x in R^* such that $a \leq x \leq b$. (The square bracket next to the name of either end-point indicates that the end-point is included; the round parenthesis indicates that it is not included.)

The concept of *open interval* is useful also in n-dimensional space R^n. A set J in the plane R^2 is an open interval if there exist four real numbers a, b, c, d such that $a < b, c < d$, and J is the set of all points (x, y) satisfying $a < x < b, c < y < d$. The extension to higher dimensions is obvious.

The *neighborhoods* of a point P in n-space R^n are by definition the open intervals that contain P. This takes care of R^1, or R, in particular, but not of R^*, since no open interval contains $+\infty$ or $-\infty$. In R^*, a set V is a *neighborhood* of a point b if (1) b belongs to V, and (2) V is either an open interval, a "half-line" $(c, +\infty]$ or $[-\infty, c)$, or the whole extended real-number system $R^* = [-\infty, \infty]$.

3. THE DEFINITION OF LIMIT

Let us look at two familiar definitions.

(1) *If f is defined for all real numbers, and a is real and k is in R^*, then the statement*

$$\lim_{x \to a} f(x) = k$$

means that to every neighborhood U of k there corresponds a neighborhood V of a such that whenever x is in V and $x \neq a$, $f(x)$ is in U.

(2) *If f is defined on a square S in the plane, and $P:(x_0, y_0)$ belongs to S, and k is in R^*, the statement*

$$\lim_{(x,y) \to (x_0,y_0)} f(x, y) = k$$

means that to every neighborhood U of k there corresponds a neighborhood V of P such that whenever (x, y) is a point of S lying in V and different from P, then $f(x, y)$ is in U.

It is easy indeed to make these look alike. First, we let D be the domain of f; in (1), D is the real-number system R, and in (2) it is S. Next, each member of D will be denoted by some single letter, such as p. In (1) we mentioned a certain family of sets, each consisting of all the points of a neighborhood V of a except for a itself; in symbols, $V - \{a\}$. (Such a set is often called a *deleted neighborhood* of a.) Let us use the letter $\mathfrak{A}$ to stand for this family of sets. In (2) we used the sets of points of S belonging to V and different from P, where V is any neighborhood of P. For this example we let $\mathfrak{A}$ stand for the family of all such sets; that is, $\mathfrak{A}$ consists of all sets of the form $V \cap S - \{P\}$, V a neighborhood of P. Now both definitions take the same form:

(3) *lim f(p) = k means that to each neighborhood U of k there corresponds a set A of the family* 𝔄 *such that for all p in A, f(p) is in U.*

A standard definition of the limit of a sequence b_1, b_2, b_3, $\cdots$ is the following:

(4) *The sequence* b_1, b_2, b_3, $\cdots$ *of real numbers has k (in R*) as limit if for each neighborhood U of k, b_n is in U for all but finitely many values of n.*

This looks a bit less like (3). But if we let D stand for the set of positive integers, and for each positive integer p we define $f(p)$ to be another notation for a_p, and then define 𝔄 to be the family of all sets A each of which consists of all but finitely many of the positive integers, (4) also takes on the same form (3). We could add other examples, but we already have enough to suggest a possible general definition of limit, as follows:

(5) *Let f be an extended-real-valued function with domain D_f, and let* 𝔄 *be any family of sets each contained in D_f. Let k be in R*. Then the statement that f(x) has k as limit (corresponding to family* 𝔄*) shall mean that whenever U is a neighborhood of k, there is a set* 𝔄 *in the family* 𝔄 *such that for every x in A, f(x) is in the neighborhood U of k.*

The trouble now is that this definition of limit has such splendid generality that we are unable to prove any interesting theorems. Since we prefer to be able to prove some theorems, we put restrictions on the family 𝔄; of course, we try to use as few restrictions as possible. We shall in fact assume that the family 𝔄 in (5) has three properties, as follows:

(6) 1. 𝔄 *is not empty; it contains at least one set* 𝔄.

   2. *Each set A in the family* 𝔄 *is nonempty; it contains at least one point of D_f.*

   3. *If A_1 and A_2 are sets belonging to the family* 𝔄*, there is a set A_3 of the family* 𝔄 *contained in both A_1 and A_2;*

$$A_3 \subset A_1 \cap A_2.$$

In our three examples these are easily verified; in fact, in both cases the family $\mathfrak{A}$ consists of infinitely many sets each with infinitely many members, and whenever A_1 and A_2 are in $\mathfrak{A}$ so is their intersection $A_1 \cap A_2$. So these requirements are not exorbitantly strong. In fact, they are satisfied for all the classical examples, and in the last section we shall see that they cannot be weakened in any respect without allowing the possibility of undesirably weird examples. On the other hand, they are strong enough, because they allow us to prove all the traditional theorems on operations with limits.

Since we shall be repeatedly using families $\mathfrak{A}$ with properties 1, 2, and 3, it is convenient to introduce some names. A family of sets satisfying 1, 2, and 3 will be called a *direction;* if all the sets A in the family $\mathfrak{A}$ are contained in a set D, $\mathfrak{A}$ is a *direction in D.* A *directed function* is a pair consisting of (a) a function f; (b) a direction in the domain of the function. Also, if $\mathfrak{A}$ is a direction, each set A of the family $\mathfrak{A}$ will be called an *advanced set.*†

Now we can state our general definition of limit for extended-real-valued functions.

(7) *Let f be an extended-real-valued function; let $\mathfrak{A}$ be a direction in the domain of f; and let k be in R^*. The statement that the directed function $(f, \mathfrak{A})$ has k as limit (in symbols, $\lim_{x, \mathfrak{A}} f(x) = k$) is defined to mean that to each neighborhood U of k there corresponds a set A in the family $\mathfrak{A}$ such that for all x in A, $f(x)$ is in U.*

SOME FUNDAMENTAL THEOREMS. The first three theorems that we shall prove make no use of the computational properties of the number system.

(8) *Let f and g be extended-real-valued functions on the respective domains D_f and D_g, and let $\mathfrak{A}$ be a direction all of whose sets are contained both in D_f and in D_g. Assume that there is a number k in R^* such that $\lim_{x, \mathfrak{A}} f(x) = k$. If there exists a set A in $\mathfrak{A}$ such that*

---

† See footnote on page 13.

$g(x) = f(x)$ *for all x in A, then*

$$\lim_{x,\,\mathfrak{A}} g(x) = k.$$

Proof: Let U be any neighborhood of k. By (7) there is a set A_1 in $\mathfrak{A}$ such that $f(x)$ is in U for all x in A. By property 1 of (6), there is a set A_2 in $\mathfrak{A}$ contained in both A and A_1. Then for all x in A_2, $f(x)$ is in U and $g(x) = f(x)$, so $g(x)$ is in U.

We now prove the important uniqueness theorem, that is, that no directed function can have more than one limit.

(9) *Let $(f, \mathfrak{A})$ be a directed function, f being extended-real-valued. If h and k are in R^*, and $h \neq k$, and $(f, \mathfrak{A})$ has k as limit, then $(f, \mathfrak{A})$ does not have h as limit.*

Proof: Let c be a number between h and k. Then k is in one of the two sets $[-\infty, c)$, $(c, \infty]$; this one we call U_1, and it is a neighborhood of k. The other we call U_2, and it is a neighborhood of h. Suppose that $(f, \mathfrak{A})$ had both h and k as limits. Since U_1 is a neighborhood of k_1, there is an A_1 in $\mathfrak{A}$ such that for all x in A_1, $f(x)$ is in U_1. Since U_2 is a neighborhood of h, there is an A_2 in $\mathfrak{A}$ such that for all x in A_2, $f(x)$ is in U_2. By property 3 of (6) there is a set A_3 in $\mathfrak{A}$ contained in both A_1 and A_2; and by property 2 of (6) there is something, say x^*, in A_3. Then x^* is in both A_1 and A_2, so $f(x^*)$ is in both U_1 and U_2. But this is impossible; U_1 and U_2 have no points in common.

(10) *If $(f, \mathfrak{A})$ is a directed function and k is in R^*, and $f(x) = k$ for all x in the domain of f, then*

$$\lim_{x,\,\mathfrak{A}} f(x) = k.$$

Proof: Let U be any neighborhood of k. Let A_1 be any member of the family $\mathfrak{A}$; such an A_1 exists by property 1 of (6). For all x in A_1, $f(x) = k$, so $f(x)$ is in U.

4. A USEFUL VERBAL DEVICE

By a verbal device due to Halmos we can word the definitions and proofs so that the language helps to draw us along the correct path. Suppose that we have a set D and a direction $\mathfrak{A}$ in D. If $P(x)$ is some sentence that has one free variable x in it, we say that "ultimately $P(x)$" (or "$P(x)$ is ultimately true") provided that there is some set† A in the direction $\mathfrak{A}$ such that for every x in A, $P(x)$ is a true statement. (Thus "ultimately" has no meaning until we have specified what the direction $\mathfrak{A}$ is.) This meaning is in accord with the colloquial meaning of "ultimately" in three important respects. First, if $P(x)$ is true for every x in D, it is also ultimately true. For by property 1 of (6) there is a set A in the direction $\mathfrak{A}$, and since $P(x)$ is true for all x in D, in particular it is true for every x in A. Second, if $P(x)$ is ultimately true it is not always false. For there is some set A in $\mathfrak{A}$ such that $P(x)$ is true for every member of A; and by property 2 of (6), A has at least one member. Third, if $P(x)$ and $Q(x)$ are two sentences, and $P(x)$ is ultimately true and $Q(x)$ is ultimately true, the compound sentence $[P(x)$ and $Q(x)]$ is ultimately true. For there is a set A_1 in $\mathfrak{A}$ such that $P(x)$ is true for every member of A_1, and there is a set A_2 in $\mathfrak{A}$ such that $Q(x)$ is true for every member of A_2. By property 3 of (6) there is a set A_3 of the family $\mathfrak{A}$ that is contained both in A_1 and in A_2. For every member x of A_3, $P(x)$ is true because x is in A_1, and $Q(x)$ is true because x is in A_2; so $[P(x)$ and $Q(x)]$ is true.

In these terms, our definition of limit takes this form:

(11) *If $(f, \mathfrak{A})$ is a directed extended-real-valued function and k is in R^*, the statement*

$$\lim_{x, \mathfrak{A}} f(x) = k$$

means that whenever U is a neighborhood of k, $f(x)$ is ultimately in U.

Proofs are correspondingly shortened. For example, in the proof of (9), after defining U_1 and U_2 we proceed thus. Since U_1 is a neighborhood of the limit k, ultimately $f(x)$ is in U_1. Similarly, ultimately $f(x)$ is in U_2. Hence, ultimately $[f(x)$ is in U_1 and

---

† At least one mathematician dislikes the phrase "advanced set." Perhaps "ultimate set," "final set," or "late set" might have been preferable.

$f(x)$ is in U_2]. But this is impossible; the bracketed statement is always false.

5. COMPUTATIONS WITH LIMITS

As yet we have not adopted any definitions of addition and multiplication with $+\infty$ and $-\infty$. We now define sums and products (both commutative) as follows:

$$\text{if } a > -\infty, \quad a + (+\infty) = a - (-\infty) = +\infty;$$

$$\text{if } a < +\infty, \quad a + (-\infty) = a - (+\infty) = -\infty;$$

$$\text{if } a > 0, \quad a(+\infty) = +\infty \quad \text{and} \quad a(-\infty) = -\infty;$$

$$\text{if } a < 0, \quad a(+\infty) = -\infty \quad \text{and} \quad a(-\infty) = +\infty;$$

$$1/(+\infty) = 0, \qquad 1/(-\infty) = 0.$$

As usual a/b will mean $a \cdot (1/b)$ whenever this has meaning. (Notice that $\infty + (-\infty)$, $0 \cdot \infty$, and ∞/∞ are undefined.)

For sums of directed functions we have the following theorem.

(12) *Let* $(f, \mathfrak{A})$ *and* $(g, \mathfrak{A})$ *be extended-real-valued functions with the same domain* D; *let* h *and* k *be in* R^*; *and let*

$$\lim_{x, \mathfrak{A}} f(x) = h, \quad \lim_{x, \mathfrak{A}} g(x) = k.$$

If the sums $f(x) + g(x)$ (x *in* D) *and* $h + k$ *are defined, the directed function* $(f + g, \mathfrak{A})$ *has a limit, and*

$$\lim_{x, \mathfrak{A}} [f(x) + g(x)] = h + k.$$

Proof: Suppose first that h and k are finite (that is, h and k are in R). Let U be any neighborhood of $(h + k)$. If e is any sufficiently small positive number, the open interval $(h + k - 2e, h + k + 2e)$ will be contained in U. Then $(h - e, h + e)$ is a neighborhood of h, so ultimately $f(x)$ is in $(h - e, h + e)$. Likewise, ultimately $g(x)$ is in $(k - e, k + e)$. Hence, ultimately

$$h - e < f(x) < h + e \quad \text{and} \quad k - e < g(x) < k + e.$$

These inequalities imply

$$h + k - 2e < f(x) + g(x) < h + k + 2e,$$

so that $f(x) + g(x)$ is in U. That is, for every neighborhood U of $h + k$, $f(x) + g(x)$ is ultimately in U, so $f(x) + g(x)$ has limit $h + k$.

Suppose that one of the numbers h, k is $+ \infty$; say $h = + \infty$. Then, because $h + k$ is defined, k is not $- \infty$, and $h + k = + \infty$. Let U be any neighborhood of $h + k$, and let c be any finite number in U; then $(c, \infty]$ is contained in U. Let b be any real number less than k; then $(b, + \infty]$ is a neighborhood of k. Ultimately $f(x)$ is in $(c - b, + \infty]$ and ultimately $g(x)$ is in $(b, + \infty]$, so ultimately

$$f(x) > c - b \quad \text{and} \quad g(x) > b,$$

whence $f(x) + g(x) > c$, and $f(x) + g(x)$ is in U. The remaining case, in which one of h, k is $- \infty$, is similarly treated.

(13) *Let $(f, \mathfrak{A})$ be an extended-real-valued function having a limit k in R^*. If k is finite, there is a set A in $\mathfrak{A}$ on which $f(x)$ is bounded; if $k \neq 0$, there is a set A in $\mathfrak{A}$ on which $1/f(x)$ is defined and bounded.*

Proof: If k is finite, $f(x)$ is ultimately in the neighborhood $(- |k| - 1, |k| + 1)$ of k, hence $|f(x)|$ has bound $|k| + 1$ on some set A in $\mathfrak{A}$. If $k < 0$, choose any finite c such that $k < c < 0$. Ultimately $f(x)$ is in $[- \infty, c)$ so that $1/f(x)$ is defined and $|1/f(x)| < 1/|c|$. Similarly for $k > 0$.

(14) *Let $(f, \mathfrak{A})$ and $(g, \mathfrak{A})$ be directed functions on the same domain D. If $f(x) g(x)$ is defined for all x in D, and*

$$\lim_{x, \mathfrak{A}} f(x) = 0,$$

and there is a set A_0 in $\mathfrak{A}$ on which $g(x)$ is bounded, then

$$\lim_{x, \mathfrak{A}} f(x) g(x) = 0.$$

Proof: Let B be a positive upper bound for $|g(x)|$ on A_0, and let U be any neighborhood of 0. Choose a positive number e so small that $-e$ and e are in U. Ultimately $f(x)$ is in the neighborhood $(-e/B, e/B)$ of 0, and ultimately $|g(x)| \leqq B$, so ultimately $[|f(x)| < e/B$ and $|g(x)| \leqq B]$. That is, ultimately $f(x) \, g(x)$ is in $(-e, +e)$, hence in U.

(15) *Let $(f, \mathfrak{A})$ and $(g, \mathfrak{A})$ be directed extended-real-valued functions on the same domain D, and having the limits h and k, respectively. If the products $f(x) \, g(x)$ $(x$ in $D)$ and hk are defined, then*

$$\lim_{x,\mathfrak{A}} f(x) \, g(x) = hk.$$

Proof: Suppose first that h and k are finite. For all x in D,

$$f(x) \, g(x) = [f(x) + (-h)] \, g(x) + h[g(x) + (-k)] + hk.$$

By (12) and (10) the factors in square brackets have limit 0, and by (13) the factors $g(x)$ and h are bounded on some set A in $\mathfrak{A}$. By (14) the first two terms in the right member have 0 as limit; by (10) the third has hk as limit. Hence by two applications of (12), $f(x)g(x)$ has hk as limit.

If one of the numbers h, k (say h) is $+\infty$, the other is not 0. Suppose first $k < 0$; then $hk = -\infty$. Let U be any neighborhood of $-\infty$. There is a negative finite number n in U, so $[-\infty, n)$ is contained in U. Also, $[-\infty, k/2)$ is a neighborhood of k, and $(2n/k, \infty]$ is a neighborhood of h (which is $+\infty$). So ultimately $f(x)$ is in $(2n/k, \infty]$ and $g(x)$ is in $[-\infty, k/2)$, so

$$f(x) > 2n/k > 0 \quad \text{and} \quad g(x) < k/2 < 0.$$

This implies

$$f(x) \, g(x) < f(x)(k/2) < n,$$

and $f(x) \, g(x)$ is in U. The case $k > 0$ is similarly treated, and also the case $h = -\infty$.

This theorem has (in view of (10)) two immediate corollaries.

(16) *If $(f,\mathfrak{A})$ is an extended-real-valued function with limit h, and k is in R^*, and the products $kf(x)$ $(x$ in $D)$ and kh are defined, then*

$$\lim_{x,\mathfrak{A}} kf(x) = kh.$$

(17) *If $(f,\mathfrak{A})$ and $(g, \mathfrak{A})$ are extended-real-valued functions on the same domain D, and have the respective limits h and k, and a and b are in R^*, and the expressions $af(x) + bg(x)$ (x in D) and $ah + bk$ are defined, then*

$$\lim_{x,\mathfrak{A}} [af(x) + bg(x)] = ah + bk.$$

(18) *If $(f,\mathfrak{A})$ and $(g, \mathfrak{A})$ are extended-real-valued functions on the same domain D and have the respective limits h and k, and the quotients $f(x)/g(x)$ (x in D) and h/k are defined, then*

$$\lim_{x,\mathfrak{A}} \frac{f(x)}{g(x)} = \frac{h}{k}.$$

Proof: Since h/k is defined, k is not 0. Suppose first that k is finite. Then on some set A of $\mathfrak{A}$ the quotient $1/g(x)$ is defined and bounded, and

$$\frac{1}{g(x)} = \frac{1}{g(x)} - \frac{1}{k} + \frac{1}{k}$$

$$= \frac{1}{k}\cdot\frac{1}{g(x)} [k - g(x)] + \frac{1}{k}.$$

The function in square brackets has limit 0, so by (14) and (16) the first term in the right member has limit 0, and by (10) and (12) $1/g(x)$ has limit $1/k$. If k is not finite, it is $+\infty$ or $-\infty$. Let $U = (c, d)$ be a neighborhood of 0. If $k = +\infty$, ultimately $g(x) > 1/d$; if $k = -\infty$, ultimately $g(x) < 1/c$, and in either case, ultimately $c < 1/g < d$, so $g(x)$ is in U. That is, $1/g(x)$ has limit 0, which is the same as $1/k$; so $1/g(x)$ has limit $1/k$ whenever $k \neq 0$. By (15), $f(x) [1/g(x)]$ has limit $h[1/k]$.

A frequently useful theorem on sequences states that if b_1, b_2, b_3, $\cdots$ is a monotonically increasing sequence (so that $b_1 \leqq b_2 \leqq b_3 \leqq \cdots$) and the b_n have an upper bound, then $\lim_{n\to\infty} b_n$ exists. Monotoneity does not generalize to arbitrary domains. But if the sequence is monotone, it has the property that for each positive integer m, ultimately $b_n \geqq b_m$. This suffices for the proof, and has an obvious generalization to directed functions. In fact, we shall improve the theorem slightly.

(19) *Let* $(f, \mathfrak{A})$ *be an extended-real-valued directed function. If for
every* x' *in* D *and every number* h *less than* $f(x')$ *it is ultimately
true that* $f(x) > h$, *then* $\lim\limits_{x,\mathfrak{A}} f(x)$ *exists and is equal to the supremum* M *of the values of* $f(x)$ *on* D.

Proof: If $M = -\infty$, $f(x)$ must be $-\infty$ for all x, so its limit is
$-\infty$. Otherwise, let U be any neighborhood of M. In U there
is a finite number c less than M, and the interval $(c, M]$ is contained in U. By definition of M, there is an x' in D such that
$f(x') > c$. Hence, by hypothesis, ultimately $f(x) > c$. But always
$f(x) \leqq M$, so ultimately $f(x)$ is in $(c, M]$ and therefore in U.

Examples. Suppose first that f is real-valued and has a subset
D of n-space R^n as domain. If a is in R^n and every neighborhood
V of a contains points of D other than a, the family $\mathfrak{A}$ of all sets
of the form $V \cap D - \{a\}$ is a direction in D, and $\lim\limits_{x,\mathfrak{A}} f(x)$
coincides with $\lim\limits_{x \to a} f(x)$ as usually defined.

With the same notation, let b be any point of D, and let $\mathfrak{B}$ be
the family of all sets $V \cap D$, in which V is a neighborhood of b.
This is a direction in D, and each set in $\mathfrak{B}$ contains the point b.
If for some k we have

$$\lim\limits_{x,\mathfrak{B}} f(x) = k,$$

and U is any neighborhood of k, there is a set B of the direction
$\mathfrak{B}$ such that $f(x)$ is in U for all x in B; in particular, $f(b)$ is in
U. But if $f(b)$ were different from k we could find a neighborhood
U of k that does not contain $f(b)$. So $f(b)$ must be equal to k.
(In general, if $(f, \mathfrak{A})$ is any extended-real-valued directed function with limit k, $f(x)$ must equal k for each point x that belongs
to every one of the advanced sets.) The statement that $\lim\limits_{x,\mathfrak{B}} f(x)$
exists is therefore equivalent to the statement that to each
neighborhood U of $f(b)$ there corresponds a neighborhood V of b
such that for every x of the domain D that is contained in V, $f(x)$
is in U. But this is the definition of the statement that f is continuous at b. Therefore the theorems of the preceding sections
reduce to familiar forms; constant functions are continuous,

and if f and g are defined in D and both continuous at b, then so are $a_1 f + a_2 g$, $f \cdot g$, and f/g if they are defined in D.

The limit of a double sequence $(f_{m,n}: m, n = 1, 2, 3, \cdots)$ is defined by defining $\mathfrak{A}$ to consist of sets $\{(m, n): m, n$ integers, $m \geqq m', n \geqq n'\}$ with m' and n' positive integers. These sets clearly form a direction in the domain D of the sequence, which is the set of all ordered pairs of positive integers.

If the domain of f is a subset D of R, and a is a real number such that for all b greater than a the set $D \cap (a, b)$ is nonempty, the class of all such sets will form a direction $\mathfrak{A}$ in D. In this case the limit of $(f, \mathfrak{A})$, if it exists, is called the "right limit" of f at a, and is often denoted by $f(a +)$. The "left limit," $f(a -)$, is analogously defined.

Suppose that f is a real-valued function on a domain D. Unless D is a finite set we cannot add all the values of f. But whenever F is a finite subset of D we can add all the corresponding values of f, obtaining a sum

$$S(F) = \sum_{x \text{ in } F} f(x).$$

This function S is real-valued, but its domain (let us call it $\mathfrak{F}$) consists of all finite subsets of D, and is not a set of numbers. We are interested in what happens when we choose larger and larger sets F. So for each finite subset F_0 of D we define $A[F_0]$ to be the set of all finite subsets of D that contain F_0. Then $A[F_0]$ is a nonempty subset of the domain $\mathfrak{F}$ of the sum-function S. The family of all sets $A[F_0]$, for all sets F_0 in $\mathfrak{F}$, we call $\mathfrak{A}$. It clearly satisfies conditions 1 and 2 of the definition of direction. Let $A[F_1]$ and $A[F_2]$ be any two members of $\mathfrak{A}$. Then $A[F_1 \cup F_2]$ is also a member of $\mathfrak{A}$, and every finite subset F of D that contains $F_1 \cup F_2$ contains F_1 (and is therefore in $A[F_1]$) and contains F_2 (and is therefore in $A[F_2]$). Hence $\mathfrak{A}$ is a direction. If $\lim_{F, \mathfrak{A}} S(F)$ exists, it is called the *unconditional sum* of the function f. (But if D happens to be the set of positive integers, so that f is a sequence $(f(n): n = 1, 2, 3, \cdots)$, the unconditional sum of f is usually called the sum of the *series* $f(1) + f(2) + \cdots$, and if the unconditional sum exists the "series" is called *uncondi-*

tionally convergent. Similar customs prevail where the domain of f is the set of all integers, or the set of ordered pairs of positive integers, etc.). This example was, to the best of the writer's knowledge, the first kind of limit treated by methods independent of structural peculiarities of the domain.†

Let f be a real-valued function on a closed interval $[a, b]$ in R. This time we shall let $\mathfrak{F}$ be the set of all finite subsets of the open interval (a, b). For each such set F we first arrange its members in increasing order, say $F = \{t_1, \cdots, t_n\}$ where $t_1 < t_2 < \cdots < t_n$, and then form the three sums:

$$T_F[a, b] = |f(t_1) - f(t_0)|$$
$$+ |f(t_2) - f(t_1)| + \cdots + |f(t_{n+1}) - f(t_n)|,$$

where we understand $t_0 = a$ and $t_{n+1} = b$;

$$P_F[a, b] = \Sigma_+ \{f(t_j) - f(t_{j-1})\},$$

where Σ_+ means the sum over all those values of j for which $f(t_j) - f(t_{j-1}) \geqq 0$;

$$N_F[a, b] = -\Sigma_- \{f(t_j) - f(t_{j-1})\},$$

where Σ_- means the sum over all those values of j for which $f(t_j) - f(t_{j-1}) \leqq 0$. We define the advanced sets $A[F]$ and the direction $\mathfrak{A}$ just as in the preceding example. Suppose that F differs from F' only in having one more point; say that F results by adjoining c to F', where $t_{k-1} < c < t_k$. In the sums defining $T_F[a, b]$ and $T_{F'}[a, b]$ the only difference is that the term

$$|f(t_k) - f(t_{k-1})|$$

in $T_{F'}[a, b]$ is missing, and in its place is the pair of terms

$$|f(c) - f(t_{k-1})| + |f(t_k) - f(c)|,$$

whose sum is not less than $|f(t_k) - f(t_{k-1})|$. So

$$T_F[a, b] \geqq T_{F'}[a, b].$$

---

† E. H. Moore, "Definition of limit in general analysis," *Proceedings of the National Academy of Sciences,* U.S.A., vol. 1, (1915), p. 628.

By induction, if F is any set in $A[F]$, that is, if F is any finite subset of (a, b) that contains F', we have

$$T_F[a, b] \geqq T_{F'}[a, b].$$

That is, for each F' in $\mathfrak{F}$, ultimately

$$T_F[a, b] \geqq T_{F'}[a, b].$$

By (19),

$$\lim_{F, \mathfrak{A}} T_F[a, b]$$

exists and is the same as the supremum of $T_F[a, b]$ for all F in $\mathfrak{F}$. In the same way, the limits of $P_F[a, b]$ and $N_F[a, b]$ exist and are equal to their suprema. These limits are called respectively the *total variation*, the *positive variation*, and the *negative variation* of f over $[a, b]$, and are denoted by $T[a, b]$, $P[a, b]$, $N[a, b]$, respectively. They are nonnegative, and may be finite or $+ \infty$.

Since by definition of Σ_+ and Σ_- we clearly have

$$T_F[a, b] = P_F[a, b] + N_F[a, b],$$

by (12) we have

$$T[a, b] = P[a, b] + N[a, b].$$

In particular, if $T[a, b]$ is finite, so are $P[a, b]$ and $N[a, b]$. In this case, however, from the identity

$$f(b) - f(a) = P_F[a, b] - N_F[a, b]$$

(proved by noticing that in the sum in the right member all terms except $f(b)$ and $-f(a)$ cancel each other), together with (17), we obtain

$$f(b) - f(a) = P[a, b] - N[a, b].$$

As a final example, let R be a rectangle in the plane. Suppose that to each rectangle r contained in R there is a nonnegative number $m(r)$ assigned, and that when r is cut into two disjoint rectangles r' and r'' we have $m(r') + m(r'') = m(r)$. For instance, $m(r)$ could be the area of r. Or, if we think of the plane as composed of a sheet of matter, not necessarily uniform, $m(r)$ could be the mass of the matter in rectangle r. By a *partition* P of R we shall mean a set consisting of (1) a finite number of rectangles $r_1, \cdots, r_k$, without common points, whose union is R, and (2) the same number of points $p_1, \cdots, p_k$, the point p_i belonging to rectangle r_i $(i = 1, \cdots, k)$. If f is defined and real-valued on R, for each partition P we define a "finite sum" $S_f(P)$ as follows. If P consists of rectangle $r_1, \cdots, r_k$ and points $p_1, \cdots, p_k$, then

$$S_f(P) = \sum_{i=1}^{k} f(p_i) m(r_i).$$

In particular, if $m(r)$ is the area of r, this is the familiar sum used in defining the Riemann integral. We wish to define the integral of f with respect to m as being in some sense the limit of the "finite sum" $S_f(P)$ as P "becomes finer and finer." Two different methods have been used.

First, let us define the *mesh* of P to be the longest of the diagonals of the rectangles $r_1, \cdots, r_k$ in P. Since the domain of S_f is the class of all partitions, an advanced set will be a set of partitions. Corresponding to each positive number e we let A_e be the set of all partitions with mesh less than e. The set $\mathfrak{A}$ of all A_e $(e > 0)$ is easily seen to satisfy the three conditions in (6), so it is a direction in the domain of S_f. Now if the limit

$$\lim_{P, \mathfrak{A}} S_f(P)$$

exists, it is called the Riemann-Stieltjes integral of f with respect to m over R, and denoted by some such symbol as

$$\int_R f(p) \, dm$$

(perhaps prefixed by (RS) to indicate that it is a Riemann-Stieltjes integral). If $m(r)$ is the area of r, the integral is called simply the Riemann integral of f over R.

Second, given any partition P', we could define $B(P')$ to be the set of all partitions P such that each of the rectangles $r_1, \cdots, r_k$ in P is completely contained in a single one of the rectangles in the partition P'. (Then we also say that P is a *repartition* of P'.) The set $\mathfrak{B}$ of all sets $B[P']$, for all partitions P', is easily seen to be a direction in the domain of S_f. If $\lim_{P, \mathfrak{B}} S_f(P)$

exists, it is called the *Pollard-Stieltjes integral* of f with respect to m over R. If $m(r)$ happens to be the area of r, it can be shown (not so very easily) that if either of the limits

$$\lim_{P,\,\mathfrak{A}} S_f(P), \quad \lim_{P,\,\mathfrak{B}} S_f(P)$$

exists, so does the other, and the two are equal. But for other functions m this can be false.

6. SUBDIRECTED FUNCTIONS AND CLUSTER POINTS

In forming a subsequence from a given sequence, we discard part of the domain, leaving enough still to be an infinite sequence. This could be generalized to directed functions, but it would not do everything in topology that we would like done. Instead, from a given directed function $(f, \mathfrak{A})$ we form a subdirected function $(f, \mathfrak{A}')$ by discarding points from each A in $\mathfrak{A}$, leaving enough still to satisfy the requirement (6). Precisely, a direction $\mathfrak{A}'$ is a subdirection of a direction $\mathfrak{A}$ provided that each set A in $\mathfrak{A}$ contains a set A' of the family $\mathfrak{A}'$. If f is a function and $\mathfrak{A}$ and $\mathfrak{A}'$ are directions in its domain, $(f, \mathfrak{A}')$ is a subdirected function (of $(f, \mathfrak{A})$) if and only if $\mathfrak{A}'$ is a subdirection of $\mathfrak{A}$. It is now easy to prove that if $(f, \mathfrak{A})$ has a limit k, so has $(f, \mathfrak{A}')$. For if U is any neighborhood of k, there is an A in $\mathfrak{A}$ such that $f(x)$ is in U for all x in A. But A contains a set A' of the subdirection $\mathfrak{A}'$; for every x in A', x is in A, so $f(x)$ is in U.

Subsequences, of course, are examples of subdirected functions. If f has domain D in R, and b is in R, and for every real number c greater than b the set $D \cap (b, c)$ is nonempty, the family $\mathfrak{A}'$ of such sets has already been seen to be a direction in D, and $\lim_{x,\,\mathfrak{A}'} f(x)$ is called $f(b +)$ if it exists. If we define $\mathfrak{A}$ to be the family of sets $V \cap D - \{b\}$, (V any neighborhood of b), this is a direction, and $\mathfrak{A}'$ is a subdirection of it. Hence if

$$\lim_{x,\,\mathfrak{A}} f(x) \quad (\text{that is, } \lim_{x \to b} f(x))$$

exists, so does $f(b +)$, and the two are equal.

If f is a sequence $(f(n): n = 1, 2, 3, \cdots)$ of real numbers, we have defined the unconditional sum $\Sigma f(n)$ by constructing the family $\mathfrak{F}$ of all finite subsets of the positive integers, and for each F_1 in $\mathfrak{F}$ defining $A[F_1]$ to be the set of all F in $\mathfrak{F}$ which contain F_1. Suppose now that $\mathfrak{A}'$ is the set of all consecutive finite sets $\{1\}, \{1, 2\}, \cdots, \{1, 2, \cdots, n\}, \cdots$, and that $A'[F_1]$ is the set of all those consecutive sets that contain F_1. The family $\mathfrak{A}'$ of all these $A'[F_1]$, for all F_1 in $\mathfrak{F}$, satisfies (6), and $A[F_1]$ contains $A'[F_1]$. So if the unconditional sum $\lim_{F,\mathfrak{A}} S(F)$ exists so does $\lim_{F,\mathfrak{A}'} S(F')$, and the two are equal. But if F' is $\{1, \cdots, n\}$, $S(F')$ is $f(1) + f(2) + \cdots + f(n)$, and this last limit is the ordinary (or simple) sum of the series $f(1) + f(2) + \cdots$. Therefore if a series is unconditionally convergent, it is (simply) convergent to the same sum.

Let us return to the definitions of the Riemann-Stieltjes and Pollard-Stieltjes integrals. The former was the limit of $S_f(P)$ with respect to the direction $\mathfrak{A}$; each member of $\mathfrak{A}$ is a set A_e ($e > 0$), and A_e is the set of all partitions P of mesh less than e. The latter was the limit of $S_f(P)$ with respect to the direction $\mathfrak{B}$; each member of $\mathfrak{B}$ is a set $B(P')$, P' being a partition, and $B(P')$ is by definition the set of all repartitions of P'. Given any set A_e in $\mathfrak{A}$, let P' be a member of A_e. Then every partition P in $B(P')$ is a repartition of P', and cannot have mesh larger than the mesh of P', which is less than e; so each P in $B(P')$ is in A_e, and A_e contains $B(P')$. That is, $\mathfrak{B}$ is a subdirection of $\mathfrak{A}$. Hence whenever the Riemann-Stieltjes integral

$$\int_R f(p) \, dm$$

exists, the Pollard-Stieltjes integral also exists and has the same value. (The converse can be shown to be false.)

It is quite possible for each of two directions $\mathfrak{A}$ and $\mathfrak{B}$ to be subdirections of the other. If these are both in the domain of a function f, then $(f, \mathfrak{A})$ and $(f, \mathfrak{B})$ are subdirected functions of each other. So if either has a limit, the other also has the same limit. In this case $\mathfrak{A}$ and $\mathfrak{B}$ are called *equivalent* directions.

Suppose, for instance, that in R^n we had preferred to use spheres centered at a point p as its neighborhoods, instead of using open intervals as we did. If f is extended-real-valued on a domain D in R^n, and b is in R^n, in order to define $\lim_{p \to b} f(p)$ we defined $\mathfrak{A}$ to be the family of all sets $V \cap D - \{b\}$, provided that no such set was empty; V was any neighborhood of b, that is, any open interval containing b. Now let $\mathfrak{B}$ be the family of all sets $S \cap D - \{b\}$, when S is any sphere $\{p : \text{dist } (p, b) < r\}$ centered at b. Every such sphere S contains an open interval V to which b belongs, and every open interval V containing b also contains a sphere S centered at b. So $\mathfrak{A}$ and $\mathfrak{B}$ are equivalent, and if either of the limits

$$\lim_{p, \mathfrak{A}} f(p), \quad \lim_{p, \mathfrak{B}} S(p)$$

exists, the other also exists and has the same value. Thus in defining $\lim_{p \to b} f(p)$ it makes no difference whether we use interval neighborhoods of b or spheres centered at b.

Similarly, in defining the limit of a sequence $(f(n): n = 1, 2, 3, \cdots)$ some people prefer to use all the sets A consisting of all but finitely many positive integers; others use all the sets of the form $m, m + 1, m + 2, \cdots$ in which m is a positive integer. The two directions are equivalent, so it is immaterial which we use in the definition.

7. THE IMPORTANCE OF CONDITIONS (6)

In Section 3 the comparison of several definitions of limit led us to the general formulation (5). But we said then that if we wish to prove any interesting theorem we need to restrict the families $\mathfrak{A}$ somehow. Suppose that $\mathfrak{A}$ is a family of sets and that D is some set containing all the sets A belonging to the family $\mathfrak{A}$. If the definition (5) is to lead to a theory worth thinking about, the following three assertions should all be true:

(20) *There is at least one extended-real-valued function f on D and at least one number k in R^* such that*

$$\lim_{x, \mathfrak{A}} f(x) = k.$$

(21) *There is at least one extended-real-valued function f on D and at least one number k in R* for which the statement*

$$\lim_{x,\mathfrak{A}} f(x) = k$$

is false.

(22) *If f and g are real-valued functions on D and*

$$\lim_{x,\mathfrak{A}} f(x) = \lim_{x,\mathfrak{A}} g(x) = 1,$$

then

$$\lim_{x,\mathfrak{A}} [f(x) + g(x)] = 2.$$

For if (20) fails there are no limits to talk about; if (21) fails the statement

$$\lim_{x,\mathfrak{A}} f(x) = k$$

yields no information; and (22) is the least we can ask if we wish to compute with limits.

Suppose then that (20) is true. By definition (5), wherever U is a neighborhood of k there is an A in $\mathfrak{A}$ such that $\cdots$ (the rest doesn't matter!). That is, property 1 of (6) holds. Suppose next that (21) holds. By (5), the falsity of the statement

$$\lim_{x,\mathfrak{A}} f(x) = k$$

is equivalent to:

There exists a neighborhood U of k such that for every set A in $\mathfrak{A}$, there is at least one x in A such that $f(x)$ is not in U.

But then each A in $\mathfrak{A}$ must contain at least one point x, and property 2 of (6) holds.

Finally, suppose that (22) holds. Let A_1 and A_2 belong to $\mathfrak{A}$. Define f and g on D, by setting $f(x) = 1$ if x is in A_1 and $f(x) = 0$ if x is not in A_1, and setting $g(x) = 1$ if x is in A_2 and $g(x) = 0$ if x is not in A_2. Then

$$\lim_{x,\mathfrak{A}} f(x) = 1,$$

for in (5) we take A to be A_1 no matter what U is, and find that $f(x)$ is in U for all x in A. Likewise

$$\lim_{x,\mathfrak{A}} g(x) = 1.$$

By (22) we must have

$$\lim_{x,\mathfrak{A}} [f(x) + g(x)] = 2.$$

Let U be the neighborhood $(\frac{3}{2}, \frac{5}{2})$ of 2. By (5), there is a set A_3 in $\mathfrak{A}$ such that for all x in A_3, $f(x) + g(x)$ is in U. But if $f(x) + g(x)$ is in U, it is greater than $\frac{3}{2}$, so $f(x)$ and $g(x)$ must both be 1, and x must be both in A_1 and in A_2. Hence every point x of the set A_3 belongs both to A_1 and to A_2, and property 3 of (6) holds.

Thus we have shown that conditions (6) cannot be weakened in any way without losing at least one of the three theorems (20), (21), (22).

8. NETS AND FILTERS

The convergence theory of Moore and Smith is based on the idea of a particular kind of partial ordering. Let D be a set and $\succ$ a binary relation in D, so that whenever x and y are in D the symbol "$x \succ y$" is either a true statement or a false statement. (It can be read "x is beyond y.") The set D is *directed by* the relation $\succ$ if

(23a) *whenever x, y, and z are in D and $x \succ y$ and $y \succ z$, it is true that $x \succ z$, and*

(23b) *whenever x and y are in D, there exists an element z of D such that $z \succ x$ and $z \succ y$.*

A *net*† is a pair $(f, \succ)$ consisting of a function f and a relation $\succ$ that directs the domain of f.

---

† The name is due to J. L. Kelley, "Convergence in topology," *Duke Mathematical Journal*, vol. 17, 1950, pp. 277–283.

(24) *If* (f, $>$) *is a net, and f is extended-real-valued on its domain D and k is in R^*, the statement*

$$\lim_{x,>} f(x) = k$$

means that for every neighborhood U of k there is an x_U in D such that for all x in D such that $x > x_U$, $f(x)$ is in U.

This is already practically in the form (5). For each x_0 in D let $A[x_0]$ be the set of all x in D such that $x > x_0$; we call this a "final section" of D. The family $\mathfrak{A}$ of all final sections satisfies (6), since with the notation of (23b) we have

$$A[z] \subset A[x] \cap A[y].$$

In fact, the Moore-Smith theory is, apart from notation, almost entirely concerned with the final sections of D; the relation $>$ serves to define the final sections, and they do the rest. This is the meaning of the statement in the introduction that the present theory is a modification of the Moore-Smith theory.

We shall not describe the theory of filters, due to H. Cartan† and also (apparently independently and approximately simultaneously) to H. L. Smith.‡ The equivalence of the theory of nets and the theory of filters has been very lucidly written up by Bartle.§ Although Bartle did not consider directed functions as we have here defined them, he gives two constructions to show that limits of filters are also limits of suitably constructed nets. The same constructions, with only notational changes, apply to directed functions too. So every net (f, $>$) can be replaced quite easily by a directed function (f, $\mathfrak{A}$), the f being unchanged and the $\mathfrak{A}$ being the final sections of its domain; and every directed

---

† H. Cartan, "Théorie des filtres," *Comptes rendus de l'académie des sciences*, ser. V, vol. 205, 1937, p. 595. The theory is used throughout the volumes of Bourbaki.

‡ H. L. Smith, "A general theory of limits," *National Mathematics Magazine*, vol. 12, 1938, p. 371.

§ R. G. Bartle, "Nets and filters in topology," *American Mathematical Monthly*, vol. 62, 1955, pp. 551–557.

function $(f, \mathfrak{A})$ can be replaced by a net $(g, \succ)$, but not so easily and at the cost of replacing f by a more complicated function g. It is even easier to show directly that directed functions and filters also have equal generality.

The fullest account in English of the theory of directed functions and their uses in topology and analysis is contained in *Real Analysis*, by E. J. McShane and T. A. Botts (Van Nostrand, 1959). An earlier paper by McShane† uses somewhat different terminology. There is also an account (with different terminology) in the beginning of *Lezioni sulle trasformazioni lineari*, by Gaetano Fichera (Istituto Matematico, Università, Trieste, 1954). This is quite readable if you happen to read Italian. (As I found later, it is also mentioned in Bourbaki, but not developed extensively; "he" prefers filters.)

For the theory of nets (Moore-Smith theory) J. L. Kelley's *General Topology* (Van Nostrand, 1955) can be strongly recommended. The theory is presented in Chapter 2, and used thereafter whenever limits are needed.

---

† E. J. McShane, "A theory of convergence," *Canadian Journal of Mathematics*, vol. 22, (1955), pp. 325–332.

A GENERALIZED WEIERSTRASS APPROXIMATION THEOREM

M. H. Stone

1. INTRODUCTION

Some years ago the writer discovered a generalization of the Weierstrass approximation theorem suggested by an inquiry into certain algebraic properties of the continuous real functions on a topological space.[1] This generalization has since shown itself to be very useful in a variety of similar situations. Interest in it has stimulated several improvements in the proof originally given and has led to some modifications and extensions of the theorem itself. At the same time many interesting applications to classical problems of analysis have been observed by those working with the generalized approximation theorem. The writer, for instance, has noted a number of such applications in his lectures of 1942–1945, dealing with this and other subjects. Since the proofs thus obtained for several important classical theorems are remarkably simple, there would seem to be some advantage in collecting the relevant material in an expository article where everything could be presented in the light of our most recent knowledge. To offer such an article is our present purpose.

2. LATTICE FORMULATIONS OF THE GENERALIZED THEOREM

The Weierstrass approximation theorem states, of course, that any continuous real function defined on a bounded closed interval of real numbers can be uniformly approximated by polynomials. The generalization with which we shall be concerned here seeks in the first instance to lighten the restrictions imposed on the domain over which the given functions are defined. The difficulty which has to be met at the very outset in formulating such a generalization is that there are no polynomials on a general domain. It is rather easy, however, to circumvent this difficulty by orienting our inquiry towards the solution of the following question: What functions can be built from the functions of a prescribed family by the application of the algebraic operations (addition, multiplication, and multiplication by real numbers) and of uniform passages to the limit? In the classical case settled by the Weierstrass approximation theorem, the prescribed family consists of just two functions, f_1 and f_2, where $f_1(x) = 1$ and $f_2(x) = x$ for all x in the basic interval. In this, as in other cases which will be noted below, the answer is especially interesting, because a very small prescribed family suffices to generate a very much more inclusive family. In his first discussion of the general problem posed above, the author focused attention on the role played in approximation theory by the operations of forming the maximum and the minimum of a pair of functions. The reason why these operations are technically appropriate to the end in view can be seen even in the classical case of Weierstrass. There it is geometrically evident that a given continuous real function can be uniformly approximated by continuous piecewise linear functions, since to obtain such approximations one has only to inscribe polygons in the graph of the given function; and each piecewise linear function can be obtained from linear functions by means of the operations in question. The approximation of piecewise linear functions by polynomials then becomes the issue. The parts of the author's proof which involve these operations have since been much improved by Kakutani, with the aid of suggestions made by Chevalley, and the results given explicit formulation as a theorem about lattices of continuous functions.[2] Further modifications will be indicated below in the course of our present discussion.

In accordance with the preceding remarks, we shall start with an arbitrary topological space X, the family $\mathfrak{X}$ of all continuous real functions on X, and a prescribed subfamily $\mathfrak{X}_0$ of $\mathfrak{X}$. Our object is to determine the family $\mathfrak{U}(\mathfrak{X}_0)$ of all those functions which can be built from functions in $\mathfrak{X}_0$ by the application of specified algebraic operations and uniform passage to the limit. We shall consider first the case where the specified operations are the lattice operations $\cup$ and $\cap$ defined as follows:

$$f \cup g = \max (f, g) \quad \text{and} \quad f \cap g = \min (f, g)$$

are the functions h and k, respectively, where

$$h(x) = \max (f(x), g(x)) \quad \text{and} \quad k(x) = \min (f(x), g(x))$$

for all x in X. Later we shall take up other cases. In general we shall require of X that it be a compact space or even a compact Hausdorff space; but in the course of our preliminary remarks no such restriction will be necessary.

In all the cases we shall consider, $\mathfrak{U}(\mathfrak{X}_0)$ is a part of $\mathfrak{X}$ closed under uniform passage to the limit—in symbols,

$$\mathfrak{U}(\mathfrak{X}_0) \subset \mathfrak{X}, \qquad \mathfrak{U}(\mathfrak{U}(\mathfrak{X}_0)) = \mathfrak{U}(\mathfrak{X}_0).$$

Let us discuss these statements briefly in the case of the lattice operations. Since $f \cup g$ and $f \cap g$ are continuous whenever f and g are continuous (the mapping of X into the plane given by $x \longrightarrow (f(x), g(x))$ is continuous, and the mappings of the plane into the real number system given by

$$(\xi, \eta) \longrightarrow \max (\xi, \eta) \quad \text{and} \quad (\xi, \eta) \longrightarrow \min (\xi, \eta)$$

respectively, are both continuous so that the composite mappings

$$x \longrightarrow \max (f(x), g(x)) \quad \text{and} \quad x \longrightarrow \min (f(x), g(x))$$

are continuous also) and since the uniform limit of continuous functions is a continuous function, we see that the operations applied in the construction of $\mathfrak{U}(\mathfrak{X}_0)$ work entirely within $\mathfrak{X}$ and hence that $\mathfrak{U}(\mathfrak{X}_0) \subset \mathfrak{X}$. We now observe that $\mathfrak{U}(\mathfrak{X}_0)$ can be constructed in two steps: we first form all the functions obtainable by applying the algebraic operations alone to members of $\mathfrak{X}_0$, and we then form all the functions obtainable from these by uniform passage to the limit. For convenience let us designate the family of functions obtained in the first step by $\mathfrak{U}_1(\mathfrak{X}_0)$, and the family obtained in the second step by $\mathfrak{U}_2(\mathfrak{X}_0)$. It is evident that

$$\mathfrak{X}_0 \subset \mathfrak{U}_1(\mathfrak{X}_0) \subset \mathfrak{U}_2(\mathfrak{X}_0) \subset \mathfrak{U}(\mathfrak{X}).$$

We shall show that $\mathfrak{U}_2(\mathfrak{X}_0)$ is closed under the operations allowed and hence that $\mathfrak{U}(\mathfrak{X}_0) = \mathfrak{U}_2(\mathfrak{X}_0)$. It is then trivial that $\mathfrak{U}(\mathfrak{X}_0)$ is also closed under those operations. It is easy to see that any function f which is a uniform limit of functions f_n in $\mathfrak{U}_2(\mathfrak{X}_0)$ is itself a member of $\mathfrak{U}_2(\mathfrak{X}_0)$; in fact, each f_n can be uniformly approximated by functions in $\mathfrak{U}_1(\mathfrak{X}_0)$ so that, if ϵ is any positive number, f_n and a corresponding function g_n in $\mathfrak{U}_1(\mathfrak{X}_0)$ can be found satisfying the inequalities

$$|f(x) - f_n(x)| < \epsilon/2, \qquad |f_n(x) - g_n(x)| < \epsilon/2,$$

and hence the inequality

$$|f(x) - g_n(x)| < \epsilon$$

for all x in X. It is also fairly easy to see that whenever f and g are in $\mathfrak{U}(\mathfrak{X}_0)$, so also are $f \cup g$ and $f \cap g$. For this it is sufficient to observe that when f and g are uniform limits of the respective sequences f_n and g_n in $\mathfrak{U}_1(\mathfrak{X}_0)$, then $f \cup g$ and $f \cap g$ are uniform limits of the respective sequences $f_n \cup g_n$ and $f_n \cap g_n$—which are obviously in $\mathfrak{U}_1(\mathfrak{X}_0)$ too. The validity of this observation depends upon the inequalities

$$|\max(\xi, \eta) - \max(\xi', \eta')| \leq |\xi - \xi'| + |\eta - \eta'|,$$

$$|\min(\xi, \eta) - \min(\xi', \eta')| \leq |\xi - \xi'| + |\eta - \eta'|,$$

for which formal proofs based on the equations

(*)
$$\max\ (\xi,\ \eta) = \tfrac{1}{2}(\xi + \eta + |\xi - \eta|)$$
$$\min\ (\xi,\ \eta) = \tfrac{1}{2}(\xi + \eta + |\xi - \eta|)$$

are easily given. Using these inequalities and choosing n so that

$$|f(x) - f_n(x)| < \epsilon/2, \qquad |g(x) - g_n(x)| < \epsilon/2$$

for all x in X, we find directly that

$$|\max\ (f(x),\ g(x)) - \max\ (f_n(x),\ g_n(x))| < \epsilon,$$

$$|\min\ (f(x),\ g(x)) - \min\ (f_n(x),\ g_n(x))| < \epsilon,$$

for x in X. In case we assume X to be compact, every function in X is automatically bounded. By virtue of this assumption, or by virtue of a direct restriction to the bounded continuous functions on X in the general case, we put ourselves in a position to summarize the preceding remarks in a particularly brief form. In fact, if we restrict $\mathfrak{X}$ to consist of the bounded continuous functions and define the distance between two bounded functions f and g to be $\sup\limits_{x \in X} |f(x) - g(x)|$, we thereby make $\mathfrak{X}$ into a complete metric space in which metric convergence is equivalent to uniform convergence. The lattice operations are continuous with respect to this metric. As before, when $\mathfrak{X}_0 \subset \mathfrak{X}$ the relations

$$\mathfrak{X}_0 \subset \mathfrak{U}(\mathfrak{X}_0) \subset \mathfrak{X}, \qquad \mathfrak{U}(\mathfrak{X}_0) = \mathfrak{U}(\mathfrak{U}(\mathfrak{X}_0))$$

are valid. The first states that the uniform limit of bounded continuous functions is a bounded continuous function, the second that $\mathfrak{U}(\mathfrak{X}_0)$ is metrically and algebraically closed. The proof of the latter fact runs as before; but it can be more briefly stated as follows: If $\mathfrak{U}_1(\mathfrak{X}_0)$ is the family of all "lattice polynomials" formed from $\mathfrak{X}_0$, and $\mathfrak{U}_2(\mathfrak{X}_0)$ is its metric closure, then $\mathfrak{U}_2(\mathfrak{X}_0)$ is obviously metrically closed, and the fact that it is algebraically closed with respect to the lattice operations is a simple, direct consequence of their metric continuity.

We are now ready to determine, in the important case where X is compact, what functions belong to $\mathfrak{U}(\mathfrak{X}_0)$.

THEOREM 1: *Let X be a compact space, $\mathfrak{X}$ the family of all continuous (necessarily bounded) real functions on X, $\mathfrak{X}_0$ an arbitrary subfamily of $\mathfrak{X}$, and $\mathfrak{U}(\mathfrak{X}_0)$ the family of all functions (necessarily continuous) generated from $\mathfrak{X}_0$ by the lattice operations and uniform passage to the limit. Then a necessary and sufficient condition for a function f in $\mathfrak{X}$ to be in $\mathfrak{U}(\mathfrak{X}_0)$ is that, whatever the points x, y in X and whatever the positive number ϵ, there exists a function f_{xy} obtained by applying the lattice operations alone to $\mathfrak{X}_0$ and such that*

$$|f(x) - f_{xy}(x)| < \epsilon, \qquad |f(y) - f_{xy}(y)| < \epsilon.$$

Proof: The necessity of the stated condition is trivial. It is the sufficiency which requires discussion. Starting with the functions f_{xy} in $\mathfrak{U}_1(\mathfrak{X}_0)$, we shall construct an approximate for f. Let G_y designate the open set $\{z; f(z) - f_{xy}(z) < \epsilon\}$, where x is fixed. By hypothesis x and y are in G_y, so that the union of all the sets G_y is the entire space X. The compactness of X implies the existence of points $y_1, \cdots, y_n$ such that the union of the sets $G_{y_1}, \cdots, G_{y_n}$ is still the entire space X. Setting

$$g_x = f_{xy_1} \cup \cdots \cup f_{xy_n} = \max (f_{xy_1}, \cdots, f_{xy_n}),$$

we see that for any z in X we have $z \in G_{y_k}$ for a suitable choice of k and hence

$$g_x(z) \geqq f_{xy_k}(z) > f(z) - \epsilon.$$

On the other hand, the fact that

$$f_{xy}(x) < f(x) + \epsilon$$

implies that $g_x(x) < f(x) + \epsilon$. We can now work in a similar manner with the functions g_x. Let H_x designate the open set

$$\{z; g_x(z) < f(z) + \epsilon\}.$$

Evidently x is in H_x, so that the union of all the sets H_x is the entire space X. The compactness of X implies the existence of points $x_1, \cdots, x_m$ such that the union of the sets $H_{x_1}, \cdots, H_{x_m}$ is still the entire space X. Setting

$$h = g_{x_1} \cap \cdots \cap g_{x_m} = \min (g_{x_1}, \cdots, g_{x_m}),$$

we see that for any z in X we have $z \in H_{x_k}$ for a suitable choice of k and hence

$$h(z) \leqq g_{x_k}(z) < f(z) + \epsilon.$$

On the other hand, the fact that

$$g_x(z) > f(z) - \epsilon$$

for all z and all x implies that

$$h(z) > f(z) - \epsilon$$

for all z. Thus we have $|f(z) - h(z)| < \epsilon$ for all z in X. To complete the proof we note that, since only the lattice operations have been used in constructing the functions g_x and h from the functions f_{xy}, these functions are all in $\mathfrak{U}_1(\mathfrak{X}_0)$, as desired.

We may note two simple corollaries, as follows:

COROLLARY 1: *If $\mathfrak{X}_0$ has the property that, whatever the points $x, y, x \neq y$, in X and whatever the real numbers α and β, there exists a function f_0 in $\mathfrak{X}_0$ for which $f_0(x) = \alpha$ and $f_0(y) = \beta$, then $\mathfrak{U}(\mathfrak{X}_0) = \mathfrak{X}$ —in other words, any continuous function on X can be uniformly approximated by lattice polynomials in functions belonging to the prescribed family $\mathfrak{X}_0$.*

COROLLARY 2: *If a continuous real function on a compact space X is the limit of a monotonic sequence f_n of continuous functions, then the sequence converges uniformly to f.* (Professor Andre Weil remarks that the extension to monotonic nets is immediate.)

Proof: We take $\mathfrak{X}_0$ to be the totality of functions occurring in the sequence f_n. Then $\mathfrak{U}_1(\mathfrak{X}_0) = \mathfrak{X}_0$ since monotonicity implies that $f_m \cup f_n$ coincides with one of the two functions f_m and f_n while $f_m \cap f_n$ coincides with the other. The assumption that

$$\lim_{n \to \infty} f_n(x) = f(x)$$

for every x now shows that the condition of Theorem 1 is satisfied. Hence f is in $\mathfrak{U}(\mathfrak{X}_0)$. Since $|f(x) - f_n(x)|$ decreases as n increases and since

$$|f(x) - f_N(x)| < \epsilon$$

for all x and a suitable choice of N, we see that

$$|f(x) - f_n(x)| < \epsilon$$

for all $n \geqq N$, as was to be proved.

Theorem 1 tells us that the question, "Can a given function f be approximated in terms of the prescribed family $\mathfrak{X}_0$?", has an answer depending only on the way in which f and $\mathfrak{X}_0$ behave on pairs of points in X. The contraction of a function obtained by suppressing all points of X except the two points x, y of a pair is a function of a very simple kind—it is completely described by the ordered pair (α, β) of those real numbers which are its values at x and at y, respectively. If $\mathfrak{X}_0(x, y)$ designates the family of functions obtained by contracting every function in $\mathfrak{X}_0$ in this manner, and if $\mathfrak{X}(x, y)$ has a corresponding significance, then everything depends on an examination (for all different pairs x, y) of the question, "Can a given element of $\mathfrak{X}(x, y)$ be approximated in terms of $\mathfrak{X}_0(x, y)$?" This question is that special case of our original problem in which X is a two-element space! When X has just two elements, the approximation problem can be described in slightly different language, as follows. We have to deal with all ordered pairs (α, β) of real numbers—that is, with the cartesian plane. On two such pairs we can perform the operation $\cup$ and $\cap$ defined by the equations

$$(\alpha, \beta) \cup (\gamma, \delta) = (\max (\alpha, \gamma), \max (\beta, \delta)),$$

$$(\alpha, \beta) \cap (\gamma, \delta) = (\min (\alpha, \gamma), \min (\beta, \delta)).$$

Geometrically these operations produce the upper right vertex and lower left vertex, respectively, of a rectangle with its sides parallel to the coordinate axes and one pair of opposite vertices falling on the points (α, β), (γ, δ). For any given subset S of the plane, the problem to be solved is that of finding what points can be generated from it by the above operations and passage to the limit. From what has been said above, it is clear that the points so generated constitute a closed subset S^* of the plane which contains with (α, β) and (γ, δ) the two points described above. It is also clear that this subset is the smallest set enjoying these properties and containing the given subset S. Reverting now to the interpretation of Theorem 1, we see that it can be restated in the following form: If $f \in \mathfrak{X}$, then $f \in \mathfrak{U}(\mathfrak{X}_0)$ if and only if

$$(f(x), (f(y)) \in \mathfrak{X}_0(x, y)^*$$

for every pair of distinct points x, y in X. We have not asserted that the conditions corresponding to various pairs x, y are independent of one another, nor have we asserted that every point (α, β) in $\mathfrak{X}_0(x, y)^*$ can be expressed in the form $\alpha = f(x)$, $\beta = f(y)$ for some f in $\mathfrak{U}(\mathfrak{X}_0)$. Indeed, even in the case where $\mathfrak{X}_0 = \mathfrak{U}(\mathfrak{X}_0)$, we know only that $\mathfrak{X}_0(x, y)^*$ is the closure of $\mathfrak{X}_0(x, y)$.

It is convenient to express some of the results sketched in the preceding paragraph as a formal theorem. This we do as follows:

THEOREM 2: *Let X be a compact space, $\mathfrak{X}$ the family of continuous real functions on X, and $\mathfrak{X}_0$ a subfamily of $\mathfrak{X}$ which is closed under the lattice operations and uniform passage to the limit. Then $\mathfrak{X}_0$ is completely characterized by the system of planar sets $\mathfrak{X}_0(x, y)^* = \mathfrak{X}_0(x, y)$.*

Proof: Our hypothesis that $\mathfrak{X}_0 = \mathfrak{U}(\mathfrak{X}_0)$ shows that $\mathfrak{X}_0(x, y)$ has $\mathfrak{X}_0(x, y)^*$ as its closure, as we remarked above. Let us suppose that

$$\mathfrak{Y}_0 = \mathfrak{U}(\mathfrak{Y}_0) \subset \mathfrak{X}$$

and that $\mathfrak{X}_0(x, y)^* = \mathfrak{Y}_0(x, y)^*$ for all pairs of points x, y in X. Then the conditions for f in $\mathfrak{X}$ to belong to $\mathfrak{X}_0$ are identical with those for it to belong to $\mathfrak{Y}_0$, Hence $\mathfrak{X}_0$ and $\mathfrak{Y}_0$ coincide.

We pass now to the modifications of Theorems 1 and 2 which result when we take into consideration the operations of linear algebra as well as the lattice operations. The newly admitted operations are, more precisely, addition and multiplication by real numbers. In view of the equations (*), which express the lattice operations in terms of the linear operations and the single operation of forming the absolute value, we may take the specified algebraic operations to be simply addition, multiplication by real numbers, and formation of absolute values. The remarks preliminary to Theorem 1 apply, *mutatis mutandis*, to the present situation. The family $\mathfrak{U}(\mathfrak{X}_0)$ of all functions which can be constructed from $\mathfrak{X}_0 \subset \mathfrak{X}$ by application of the linear lattice operations and uniform passage to the limit is again seen to be obtainable in two steps, the first being algebraic and the second consisting in the adjunction of uniform limits. This family is closed under the operations used to generate it. We now have the following analog of the results contained in Theorems 1 and 2.

THEOREM 3:[2] *Let X be a compact space, $\mathfrak{X}$ the family of all continuous (necessarily bounded) real functions on X, $\mathfrak{X}_0$ an arbitrary subfamily of $\mathfrak{X}$, and $\mathfrak{U}(\mathfrak{X}_0)$ the family of all functions (necessarily continuous) generated from $\mathfrak{X}_0$ by the linear lattice operations and uniform passage to the limit. Then a necessary and sufficient condition for a function f in $\mathfrak{X}$ to be in $\mathfrak{U}(\mathfrak{X}_0)$ is that f satisfy every linear relation of the form $\alpha g(x) = \beta g(y)$, $\alpha\beta \geqq 0$, which is satisfied by all functions in $\mathfrak{X}_0$. If $\mathfrak{X}_0$ is a closed linear sublattice of $\mathfrak{X}$—that is, if $\mathfrak{X}_0 = \mathfrak{U}(x_0)$—then $\mathfrak{X}_0$ is characterized by the system of all the linear relations of this form which are satisfied by every function belonging to it. The linear relations associated with an arbitrary pair of points x, y in X must be equivalent to one of the following distinct types:*

(1) *$g(x) = 0$ and $g(y) = 0$;*

(2) *$g(x) = 0$ and $g(y)$ unrestricted, or vice versa;*

(3) *$g(x) = g(y)$ without restriction on the common value;*

(4) *$g(x) = \lambda g(y)$ or $g(y) = \lambda g(x)$ for a unique value λ, $0 < \lambda < 1$.*

Proof: Since $\mathfrak{Y}_0 = \mathfrak{U}(\mathfrak{X}_0)$ is closed under the lattice operations and uniform passage to the limit, Theorem 2 can be applied to $\mathfrak{Y}_0$. However, the fact that $\mathfrak{Y}_0$ is also closed under the linear operations can be expected to produce effective simplifications. Indeed we see that the planar set $\mathfrak{Y}_0(x, y)$, where x and y are arbitrary points in X, must be the entire plane, a straight line passing through the origin, or the one-point set consisting of the origin alone. This appears at once when we observe that if

$$(\alpha, \beta) \in \mathfrak{Y}_0(x, y),$$

then

$$(\lambda\alpha, \lambda\beta) \in \mathfrak{Y}_0(x, y)$$

for every λ, and that if (α, β) and (γ, δ) are in $\mathfrak{Y}_0(x, y)$, then

$$(\alpha + \gamma, \beta + \delta) \in \mathfrak{Y}_0(x, y).$$

Since $\mathfrak{Y}_0(x, y)$ is obviously a closed subset of the plane, we have

$$\mathfrak{Y}_0(x, y)^* = \mathfrak{Y}_0(x, y).$$

When $\mathfrak{Y}_0(x, y)$ is a straight line through the origin, we write its equation as $\alpha\xi = \beta\eta$ and observe that

$$(\beta, \alpha) \in \mathfrak{Y}_0(x, y).$$

Since $\mathfrak{Y}_0$ is closed under the operation of forming absolute values, we see that

$$(|\beta|, |\alpha|) \in \mathfrak{Y}_0(x, y).$$

Hence $\alpha|\beta| = |\alpha|\beta$ so that $\alpha\beta|\beta| = |\alpha|\beta^2 \geqq 0$ and $\alpha\beta \geqq 0$. When $\mathfrak{Y}_0(x, y)$ consists of the origin alone, we have the case enumerated as (1) in the statement of the theorem. When $\mathfrak{Y}_0(x, y)$ is a straight line through the origin we have case (2) if it coincides with one of the coordinate axes, case (3) if it coincides with the bisector of the angle between the positive coordinate axes, and case (4) otherwise. When $\mathfrak{Y}_0(x, y)$ is the entire plane, there is no corresponding linear relation, of course. Theorem 2 shows that $\mathfrak{Y}_0$ is characterized by the sets

$$\mathfrak{Y}_0(x, y) = \mathfrak{Y}_0(x, y)^*$$

—in other words that f in $\mathfrak{X}$ belongs to $\mathfrak{Y}_0 = \mathfrak{U}(\mathfrak{X}_0)$ if and only if

$$(f(x), f(y)) \in \mathfrak{Y}_0(x, y).$$

Since $\mathfrak{X}_0 \subset \mathfrak{Y}_0$, it is clear that the conditions thus imposed on the functions in $\mathfrak{U}(\mathfrak{X}_0)$ are satisfied by the functions in $\mathfrak{X}_0$. On the other hand, if all the functions in $\mathfrak{X}_0$ satisfy relations of the kind enumerated in (1)–(4), it is clear that every function in $\mathfrak{U}(\mathfrak{X}_0)$ must do likewise: for the sums, constant multiples, absolute values, and uniform limits of functions which satisfy a condition of any one of these types must satisfy the same condition. Thus the linear relations of the form $\alpha g(x) = \beta g(y)$, $\alpha\beta \geqq 0$, satisfied by the functions in $\mathfrak{X}_0$ are identical with those satisfied by the functions in $\mathfrak{U}(\mathfrak{X}_0)$ and serve to characterize the latter family completely.

We may note some simple corollaries to the theorem just proved.

COROLLARY 1: *In order that* $\mathfrak{U}(\mathfrak{X}_0)$ *contain a nonvanishing constant function, it is necessary and sufficient that the only linear relations of the form* $\alpha g(x) = \beta g(y)$, $\alpha\beta > 0$, *satisfied by every function in* $\mathfrak{X}_0$ *be those reducible to the form* $g(x) = g(y)$.

Proof: It is obvious that of conditions (1)–(4) in Theorem 3, only condition (3) can be satisfied by a nonvanishing constant function.

COROLLARY 2: *In order that* $\mathfrak{U}(\mathfrak{X}_0) = \mathfrak{X}$, *it is sufficient that the functions in* $\mathfrak{X}_0$ *satisfy no linear relation of the form* (1)–(4) *of Theorem 3.*

In order to state a further corollary, we first introduce a convenient definition.

DEFINITION 1: *A family of arbitrary functions on a domain X is said to be a separating family (for that domain) if, whenever x and y are distinct points of X, there is some function f in the family with distinct values* $f(x), f(y)$ *at these points.*

In terms of this definition we have the following result.

COROLLARY 3: *If X is compact and if* $\mathfrak{X}_0$ *is a separating family for X and contains a nonvanishing constant function, then* $\mathfrak{U}(\mathfrak{X}_0) = \mathfrak{X}$.

Proof: Since $\mathfrak{X}_0$ contains a nonvanishing constant function, the only conditions of (1)–(4) satisfied by every function in $\mathfrak{X}_0$ are those of the form (3). Since $\mathfrak{X}_0$ is a separating family, no linear relation of the form $g(x) = g(y)$, where $x \neq y$, is satisfied by every function in $\mathfrak{X}_0$. Hence Corollary 2 yields the desired result.

COROLLARY 4: *If $\mathfrak{X}_0$ is a separating family, then so is $\mathfrak{X}$.   If $\mathfrak{X}$ is a separating family and $\mathfrak{U}(\mathfrak{X}_0) = \mathfrak{X}$, then $\mathfrak{X}_0$ is also a separating family.*

Proof: The first statement is trivial. The second statement follows at once from the fact that $\mathfrak{X}_0$ is subject to no linear relation of the form $g(x) = g(y)$ which is not also satisfied by every function in $\mathfrak{U}(\mathfrak{X}_0) = \mathfrak{X}$.

It should be remarked that in general the family $\mathfrak{X}$ of *all* continuous functions on a compact space X need not be a separating family. In case X is a compact *Hausdorff* space, however, it is well known that $\mathfrak{X}$ is a separating family: if $x \neq y$, there exists a continuous function f on X such that $f(x) = 0, f(y) = 1$.

3. LINEAR RING FORMULATIONS OF THE GENERALIZED THEOREM

We are now ready to discuss the approximation problem when the specified algebraic operations used in the construction of approximants are the linear operations and multiplication. Since the product of two continuous functions is continuous, we see that the family $\mathfrak{X}$ of all continuous functions of a topological space $\mathfrak{X}$ is a commutative ring with respect to the two operations of addition and multiplication, and a commutative linear associative algebra or linear ring with respect to the operations of addition, multiplication, and multiplication by real numbers. Hence the formally stated results of this section constitute what may be called the *linear-ring* formulation of the generalized Weierstrass approximation theorem.

If we now designate by $\mathfrak{U}(\mathfrak{X}_0)$ the family of all functions generated from $\mathfrak{X}_0 \subset \mathfrak{X}$ by means of the linear ring operations and uniform passage of the limit, we have to note a slight modification which must be made in the general statements made in the lattice case. If f and g are uniform limits of the sequences f_n and g_n respectively, the product fg is not in general the uniform limit of the sequence $f_n g_n$—consider, for example, the case where $g_n = g$

is a nonbounded function and f_n is the constant $1/n$. *We shall therefore suppose that* $\mathfrak{X}$ *consists of all bounded continuous functions on a topological space* X, this boundedness restriction being automatically satisfied when X is compact. By virtue of this restriction, we can apply the inequality

$$|fg - f_n g_n| \leqq |f|\,|g - g_n| + |g|\,|f - f_n| + |f - f_n|\,|g - g_n|$$

to show that when f_n and g_n are uniformly convergent sequences in $\mathfrak{X}$, their respective limits f and g are in $\mathfrak{X}$ and that the sequence $f_n g_n$ converges uniformly to the product fg, in $\mathfrak{X}$. When $\mathfrak{X}_0 \subset \mathfrak{X}$ we see as before that $\mathfrak{U}(\mathfrak{X}_0) \subset \mathfrak{X}$, $\mathfrak{U}(\mathfrak{U}(\mathfrak{X}_0)) = \mathfrak{U}(\mathfrak{X}_0)$. It is easy to see that $\mathfrak{U}(\mathfrak{X}_0)$ consists of all those functions, necessarily in $\mathfrak{X}$, which are uniform limits of polynomials in members of $\mathfrak{X}_0$—in other words, $f \in \mathfrak{X}$ is in $\mathfrak{U}(\mathfrak{X}_0)$ if and only if, whatever the positive number ϵ, there exist functions $f_1, \cdots, f_n$ and a polynomial function $p(\xi_1, \cdots, \xi_n)$ of the real variables $\xi_1, \cdots, \xi_n$ with $p(0, \cdots, 0) = 0$ such that

$$|f(x) - p(f_1(x), \cdots, f_n(x))| < \epsilon$$

for every x in X.

Now in order to prove our principal theorem, we shall establish a very special case of the classical Weierstrass approximation theorem, using for this purpose direct and elementary methods which do not depend on any general theory. The result we need is the following proposition.

THEOREM 4: *If* ϵ *is any positive number and* $\alpha \leqq \xi \leqq \beta$ *any real interval, then there exists a polynomial* $p(\xi)$ *in the real variable* ξ *with* $p(0) = 0$ *such that* $\big||\xi| - p(\xi)\big| < \epsilon$ *for* $\alpha \leq \xi \leq \beta$.

Proof: Unless the point $\xi = 0$ is inside the given interval (α, β), we can obviously take $p(\xi) = \pm \xi$. Thus there is no loss of generality in confining our attention to intervals of the form $(-\gamma, \gamma)$ where $\gamma > 0$, since the given interval (α, β) can be included in an interval of this form. Moreover it is obviously sufficient to study the case of the interval $(-1, 1)$ since, if $q(\eta)$, $q(0) = 0$, is a polynomial such that

$$\big||\eta| - q(\eta)\big| < \epsilon/\gamma$$

for $-1 \le \eta \le 1$, then

$$p(\xi) = \gamma q(\xi/\gamma), \qquad p(0) = 0,$$

is a polynomial such that $\big| |\xi| - p(\xi) \big| < \epsilon$ for $-\gamma \le \xi \le \gamma$. We shall obtain the desired polynomial q for the interval $-1 \le \eta \le 1$ as a partial sum of the power series development for $\sqrt{1 - \zeta}$ where $\zeta = 1 - \eta^2$. The validity of the development must be established directly.

We commence by defining a sequence of constants α_k recursively from the relations

$$\alpha_1 = \frac{1}{2}$$

$$\alpha_k = \frac{1}{2} \sum_{m+n=k} \alpha_m \alpha_n = \frac{1}{2} \left(\alpha_1 \alpha_{k-1} + \alpha_2 \alpha_{k-2} + \cdots + \alpha_{k-1} \alpha_1 \right)$$

It is obvious that $\alpha_k > 0$. Putting

$$\sigma_n = \sum_1^n \alpha_k,$$

we can show inductively that $\sigma_n < 1$. In fact, we have

$$\sigma_1 = \alpha_1 = \tfrac{1}{2} < 1$$

and note that $\sigma_n < 1$ implies

$$\sigma_{n+1} = \alpha_1 + \sum_{k=2}^{n+1} \alpha_k = \frac{1}{2} + \frac{1}{2} \sum_{k=2}^{n+1} \sum_{\substack{i+j=k \\ i,j \ge 1}} \alpha_i \alpha_j$$

$$\le \frac{1}{2} + \frac{1}{2} \sum_{i,j=1}^{n} \alpha_i \alpha_j \le \frac{1}{2} \left(1 + \sigma_n^2 \right) < 1.$$

Accordingly the positive term series

$$\sum_{k=1}^{\infty} \alpha_k$$

converges to a sum σ satisfying the inequality $\sigma \le 1$; and the power series

$$\sum_{k=1}^{\infty} \alpha_k \zeta^k$$

converges uniformly for $|\zeta| \leqq 1$ to a continuous function $\sigma(\zeta)$. It is now comparatively easy to identify this function with the function $1 - \sqrt{1 - \zeta}$. To do so we prove that

$$\sigma(\zeta)(2 - \sigma(\zeta)) = \zeta.$$

Looking at the partial sums of the power series for $\sigma(\zeta)$, we observe that

$$\left(\sum_{i=1}^{n} \alpha_i \zeta^i \right)\left(2 - \sum_{j=1}^{n} \alpha_j \zeta^j \right) = 2 \sum_{k=1}^{n} \alpha_k \zeta^k - \sum_{i,j=1}^{n} \alpha_i \alpha_j \zeta^{i+j}$$

$$= 2 \sum_{k=1}^{n} \alpha_k \zeta^k - 2 \sum_{k=2}^{n} \alpha_k \zeta^k - \sum_{\substack{1 \leqq i,j \leqq n}}^{i+j \geqq n+1} \alpha_i \alpha_j \zeta^{i+j}$$

$$= \zeta - \sum_{\substack{1 \leqq i,j \leqq n}}^{i+j \geqq n+1} \alpha_i \alpha_j \zeta^{i+j}$$

in accordance with the definition of the coefficients α_k. The final term here can now be estimated as follows:

$$\left| \sum_{\substack{1 \leqq i,j \leqq n}}^{i+j \geqq n+1} \alpha_i \alpha_j \zeta^{i+j} \right| \leqq \sum_{\substack{1 \leqq i,j \leqq n}}^{i+j \geqq n+1} \alpha_i \alpha_j \leqq \sum_{k=n+1}^{\infty} \sum_{\substack{i,j \geqq 1}}^{i+j=k} \alpha_i \alpha_j$$

$$\leqq 2 \sum_{k=n+1}^{\infty} \alpha_k.$$

When n becomes infinite, therefore, this term tends to zero, and passage to the limit in the identity above accordingly yields the relation

$$\sigma(\zeta)(2 - \sigma(\zeta)) = \zeta.$$

For each ζ such that $-1 \leqq \zeta \leqq 1$ we have

$$\sigma(\zeta) = 1 \pm \sqrt{1 - \zeta}.$$

Here we decide upon the choice of sign by showing that $\sigma(\zeta) \leqq 1$, an inequality incompatible with the upper sign. It is evident that $\sigma(1) = 1$, independently of the choice of sign, and hence that

$$\sum_{k=1}^{\infty} \alpha_k = \sigma(1) = 1.$$

Inasmuch as α_k is positive, it follows that

$$\sigma(\zeta) \leqq \sigma(|\zeta|) \leqq \sigma(1) = 1,$$

as we intended to show. It is now clear that the power series for $\sqrt{1 - \zeta}$ is given by

$$\sqrt{1 - \zeta} = 1 - \sigma(\zeta) = 1 - \sum_{k=1}^{\infty} \alpha_k \zeta^k = \sum_{k=1}^{\infty} \alpha_k (1 - \zeta^k).$$

Taking η so that $-1 \leqq \eta \leqq 1$, we have $0 \leqq 1 - \eta^2 \leqq 1$ and hence

$$|\eta| = \sqrt{\eta^2} = 1 - \sigma(1 - \eta^2) = \sum_{k=1}^{\infty} \alpha_k (1 - (1 - \eta^2)^k),$$

the series being uniformly convergent. The general term of this series is a polynomial in η which vanishes for $\eta = 0$. Hence we can take a suitable one of its partial sums as the required polynomial $q(\eta)$, thus completing our discussion.

We are now ready to give our principal results concerning the generalization of the Weierstrass theorem for the linear-ring operations.

THEOREM 5: *Let X be a compact space, $\mathfrak{X}$ the family of all continuous real functions on X, $\mathfrak{X}_0$ an arbitrary subfamily of $\mathfrak{X}$, and $\mathfrak{U}(\mathfrak{X}_0)$ the family of all functions (necessarily continuous) generated from $\mathfrak{X}_0$ by the linear-ring operations and uniform passage to the limit. Then a necessary and sufficient condition for a function f in $\mathfrak{X}$ to be in $\mathfrak{U}(\mathfrak{X}_0)$ is that f satisfy every linear relation of the form $g(x) = 0$ or $g(x) = g(y)$ which is satisfied by all functions in $\mathfrak{X}_0$. If $\mathfrak{X}_0$ is a closed linear subring of $\mathfrak{X}$—that is, if $\mathfrak{X}_0 = \mathfrak{U}(\mathfrak{X}_0)$—then $\mathfrak{X}_0$ is characterized by the system of all the linear relations of this kind which are satisfied by every function belonging to it. In other words, $\mathfrak{X}_0$ is characterized by the partition of X into mutually disjoint closed subsets on each of which every function in $\mathfrak{X}_0$ is constant and by the specification of that one, if any, of these subsets on which every function in $\mathfrak{X}_0$ vanishes.*

Proof: By virtue of Theorem 4, we see that if f is in $\mathfrak{U}(\mathfrak{X}_0)$, then $|f|$ is also in $\mathfrak{U}(\mathfrak{X}_0)$. Indeed, since X is compact, the function f is bounded. Assuming accordingly that

$$\alpha \leq f(x) \leq \beta$$

for all x, we can find a polynomial $p_n(\xi)$ such that

$$\big| |\xi| - p_n(\xi) \big| < 1/n$$

for $\alpha \leq \xi \leq \beta$, while $p_n(0) = 0$. It is clear that $p_n(f)$ is in $\mathfrak{U}(\mathfrak{X}_0)$ and that

$$\big| |f(x)| - p_n(f(x)) \big| < 1/n$$

for all x in X. Hence $|f|$ is the uniform limit of functions—namely, the functions $p_n(f)$. Referring to the formulas (∗) connecting the operations $\cup$ and $\cap$ with the operation of forming the absolute value, we now see that whenever f and g are in $\mathfrak{U}(\mathfrak{X}_0)$, then so also are $f \cup g$ and $f \cap g$—in other words, $\mathfrak{U}(\mathfrak{X}_0)$ is closed under the linear lattice operations, as well as under the ring operations and uniform passage to the limit. The characterization of closed linear sublattices of $\mathfrak{X}$ given in Theorem 3 applies, naturally, to $\mathfrak{U}(\mathfrak{X}_0)$. It is easy to see that none of the characteristic linear relations can be of the type (4) described there. In fact, if every function in $\mathfrak{U}(\mathfrak{X}_0)$ were to satisfy a linear relation of the form $g(x) = \lambda g(y)$, we would find for every f in $\mathfrak{U}(\mathfrak{X}_0)$ that, f^2 being also in $\mathfrak{U}(\mathfrak{X}_0)$, the relations

$$f(x) = \lambda f(y), \qquad f^2(x) = \lambda f^2(y), \qquad \lambda^2 f^2(y) = \lambda f^2(y)$$

would hold; and we would conclude that $f(y) = 0$ for every f in $\mathfrak{U}(\mathfrak{X}_0)$ or that $\lambda = 0, 1$. Thus we conclude that f is in $\mathfrak{U}(\mathfrak{X}_0)$ if and only if it satisfies all the linear relations $g(x) = 0$ or $g(x) = g(y)$ satisfied by every function in $\mathfrak{X}_0$.

The first characterization of the closed linear subrings of $\mathfrak{X}$ given in the statement of the theorem follows immediately. As to the second characterization, we remark first that the relation $\equiv$ defined by putting $x \equiv y$ if and only if $f(x) = f(y)$ for all f in $\mathfrak{X}_0$ is obviously an equivalence relation *stronger* than the natural equality in $X : x = y$ implies $x \equiv y$; $x \equiv y$ implies $y \equiv x$; $x \equiv y$ and $y \equiv z$ imply $x \equiv z$. Consequently, X is partitioned by this equivalence relation into mutually disjoint subsets, each

a maximal set of mutually equivalent elements. The set of all
points y such that $x \equiv y$ is just that partition class which contains x. Since this set is the intersection or common part of all
the sets

$$X_f = (y; f(x) = f(y))$$

for the various functions f in $\mathfrak{X}_0$ and since each set X_f is closed
by virtue of the continuity of f, we see that the partition class
containing x is closed. If x and y are in distinct partition classes,
then there exists a function f in $\mathfrak{X}_0$ such that $f(x) \neq f(y)$, since
otherwise we would have $x \equiv y$ and the two given partition
classes could not be distinct. If a partition class contains a
single point x such that $f(x) = 0$ for every f in $\mathfrak{X}_0$, then all its
points obviously have this property. On the other hand, at
most one partition class can contain such a point since, if x and y
are points such that $f(x) = 0$, $f(y) = 0$ for every f in $\mathfrak{X}_0$, then
$f(x) = f(y)$ for every f in $\mathfrak{X}_0$, $x \equiv y$, and x and y are in the same
partition class.

We cannot expect that an arbitrary partition of X into
mutually disjoint closed subsets can be derived in the manner
just described from some closed linear subring $\mathfrak{X}_0$ of $\mathfrak{X}$. However,
partitions obtained from *distinct* closed linear subrings are necessarily *distinct*—except in the case where one subring consists of
all the functions in $\mathfrak{X}$ which are constant on each partition class
and the other consists of all those functions which are in the
first subring and in addition vanish on one specified partition
class. Thus we see that a closed linear subring is specified by
the partition of X into the closed subsets on each of which all
its members are constant and the specification of that particular
partition class, if any, on which all its members vanish.

We have at once a pair of useful corollaries.

COROLLARY 1: *In order that* $\mathfrak{U}(\mathfrak{X}_0)$ *contain a nonvanishing constant function, it is necessary and sufficient that for every* x *in* X
there exist some f *in* $\mathfrak{X}_0$ *such that* $f(x) \neq 0$.

COROLLARY 2: *If* $\mathfrak{X}_0$ *is a separating family for* X, *then* $\mathfrak{U}(\mathfrak{X}_0)$
either coincides with $\mathfrak{X}$ *or is, for a uniquely determined point* x_0,

the family of all functions f in $\mathfrak{X}$ *such that* $f(x_0) = 0$. *Conversely, if* $\mathfrak{X}$ *is a separating family for* X, *and* $\mathfrak{U}(\mathfrak{X}_0)$ *either coincides with* $\mathfrak{X}$ *or is the family of all those f in* $\mathfrak{X}$ *which vanish at some fixed point* x_0 *in* X, *then* $\mathfrak{X}_0$ *is a separating family.*

Proof: If $\mathfrak{X}_0$ is a separating family, so also are $\mathfrak{U}(\mathfrak{X}_0)$ and $\mathfrak{X}$. Hence the partition classes associated with $\mathfrak{U}(\mathfrak{X}_0)$ must each consist of a single point. It follows that $\mathfrak{U}(\mathfrak{X}_0)$ must be as indicated. Conversely, when $\mathfrak{X}$ is a separating family and $\mathfrak{U}(\mathfrak{X}_0)$ is as stated, then $\mathfrak{U}(\mathfrak{X}_0)$ is a separating family. If it were not, every f in $\mathfrak{U}(\mathfrak{X}_0)$ vanishes at some point x_0; and there would exist distinct points x and y in X such that $f_0(x) = f_0(y)$ for every f_0 in $\mathfrak{U}(\mathfrak{X}_0)$. Consider now an arbitrary function f in $\mathfrak{X}$. Clearly, the function f_0 defined by putting

$$f_0(z) = f(z) - f(x_0)$$

is continuous and vanishes at x_0. Thus f_0 is in $\mathfrak{U}(\mathfrak{X}_0)$, the equation $f_0(x) = f_0(y)$ is verified, and in consequence $f(x) = f(y)$. Thus we find that $f(x) = f(y)$ for every f in $\mathfrak{X}$, against hypothesis. Since $\mathfrak{U}(\mathfrak{X}_0)$ is a separating family, $\mathfrak{X}_0$ must be also. Otherwise, of course, there would exist distinct points x, y in X such that $f_0(x) = f_0(y)$ for every f_0 in $\mathfrak{X}_0$; and then the equation $f(x) = f(y)$ would hold for every f in $\mathfrak{U}(\mathfrak{X}_0)$, contrary to what was just established.

4. THE CHARACTERIZATION OF CLOSED IDEALS

In developing effective general algebraic theories of lattices, linear lattices, and rings, it has been found useful to introduce the concept of an *ideal*. Although ideals are independently defined in the different algebraic circumstances mentioned, their theoretical roles do not differ much from one case to another. Because the results of the preceding sections easily yield characterizations of those ideals in $\mathfrak{X}$ (the family of all continuous real functions on a compact space X) which are closed under uniform passage to the limit, it seems worthwhile to digress from the main line of our discussion long enough to present the very useful facts available in this domain. This we shall now do without further detailed analysis of the concept of an ideal.

When we think of $\mathfrak{X}$ as a lattice—the only algebraic operations taken into consideration being the operations $\cup$ and $\cap$—we define an ideal $\mathfrak{X}_0$ to be a nonvoid subclass of $\mathfrak{X}$ which contains $f \cup g$ together with f and g, and which contains $f \cap g$ together with f. The second condition of this definition is evidently equivalent to the requirement that $\mathfrak{X}_0$ should contain g whenever it contains f and $f(x) \geqq g(x)$ for every x. (Because of the familiar duality between the two operations $\cup$ and $\cap$, there is also a dual definition in which the roles played here by these operations are interchanged.) We now have the following characterization of the closed ideals in $\mathfrak{X}$.

THEOREM 6: *Let $\mathfrak{X}$ be the lattice of all continuous real functions on a compact space X, $\mathfrak{X}_0$ an arbitrary subfamily of $\mathfrak{X}$, F_0 the extended-real function defined on X through the equation $F_0(x) =$ sup $f(x)$, and $\mathfrak{Y}_0$ the family of all those functions f in $\mathfrak{X}$ such that $f \in \mathfrak{X}_0$ $f(x) \leqq F_0(x)$ for every x in X. When $\mathfrak{X}_0$ is void, $F_0(x) = -\infty$ for every x and $\mathfrak{Y}_0$ is void. Otherwise, $\mathfrak{Y}_0$ is the smallest closed ideal containing $\mathfrak{X}_0$; and $\mathfrak{X}_0$ is a closed ideal if and only if $\mathfrak{X}_0 = \mathfrak{Y}_0$. A closed ideal $\mathfrak{X}_0$ is characterized by the associated function F_0.*

Proof: As indicated in the statement of the theorem, we permit $+\infty$ and $-\infty$ to appear as values of F_0, when necessary. When $\mathfrak{X}_0$ is nonvoid, it is easy to verify that $F_0(x) > -\infty$ for every x and that $\mathfrak{Y}_0$ is nonvoid and is a closed ideal in $\mathfrak{X}$. For example, if f is in $\mathfrak{Y}_0$ and $g(x) \leqq f(x)$ for every x, then obviously $g(x) \leqq F_0(x)$ for every x and g is in $\mathfrak{Y}_0$. If $\mathfrak{X}_0$ is a closed ideal, we can show that $\mathfrak{X}_0 = \mathfrak{Y}_0$. To do so we examine the relations between F_0 and the planar sets $\mathfrak{X}_0(x, y)^*$ which characterize $\mathfrak{X}_0$ as a closed sublattice of $\mathfrak{X}$ in accordance with Theorem 2. First of all, it is evident that $\mathfrak{X}_0(x, y)$ and hence also its closure $\mathfrak{X}_0(x, y)^*$ must be contained in the set of points (α, β) such that $\alpha \leq F_0(x)$ and $\beta \leq F_0(y)$. On the other hand, $(F_0(x), F_0(y))$ is a limit point of $\mathfrak{X}_0(x, y)$ and is therefore in $\mathfrak{X}_0(x, y)^*$, as will be verified at once.

If $\epsilon < 0$, then there exist functions f and g in $\mathfrak{X}_0$ such that

$$f(x) > F_0(x) - \epsilon, \qquad g(y) > F_0(y) - \epsilon$$

for any prescribed pair of points x, y in X. The function $h = f \cup g$ is in the ideal $\mathfrak{X}_0$ and satisfies the relations

$$h(x) \geqq f(x) > F(x) - \epsilon, \qquad h(y) \geqq g(y) > F_0(y) - \epsilon.$$

Thus $(h(x), h(y))$ is a point in $\mathfrak{X}_0(x, y)$ and

$$|h(x) - F_0(x)| < \epsilon, \qquad |h(y) - F_0(y)| < \epsilon,$$

so that $(F_0(x), F_0(y))$ is in $\mathfrak{X}_0(x, y)^*$ as we wished to prove.

Now we establish the fact that f is in $\mathfrak{X}_0$ when $f(x) \leq F_0(x)$ for every x. Let f_ϵ be the function in $\mathfrak{X}$ defined by putting

$$f_\epsilon(x) = f(x) - \epsilon, \qquad \epsilon > 0.$$

If x, y are arbitrary points in X, an argument similar to that just carried through shows that there exists a function h in $\mathfrak{X}_0$ satisfying the inequalities

$$h(x) > f_\epsilon(x) = f(x) - \epsilon, \qquad h(y) > f_\epsilon(y) = f(y) - \epsilon.$$

The function $f_{xy} = h \cap f_\epsilon$ then belongs to the ideal $\mathfrak{X}_0$ and has the property that

$$f(x) - f_{xy}(x) = \epsilon, \qquad f(y) - f_{xy}(y) = \epsilon.$$

By Theorem 1 we conclude that f is the uniform limit of functions in the closed ideal $\mathfrak{X}_0$ and hence that f is itself in $\mathfrak{X}_0$. We have now shown that $\mathfrak{Y}_0 \subset \mathfrak{X}_0$. Since $\mathfrak{X}_0 \subset \mathfrak{Y}_0$ by construction, we conclude that $\mathfrak{X}_0 = \mathfrak{Y}_0$ under the present hypothesis.

Returning to the case where $\mathfrak{X}_0$ is an arbitrary nonvoid family, we consider a closed ideal $\mathfrak{X}_1$ containing $\mathfrak{X}_0$. Evidently $\mathfrak{X}_1$ has an associated function F_1 such that $F_1(x) \geqq F_0(x)$ for every x. Hence

$$\mathfrak{X}_1 = \mathfrak{Y}_1 \subset \mathfrak{Y}_0.$$

Thus $\mathfrak{Y}_0$ is the smallest closed ideal containing $\mathfrak{X}_0$. With this the proof of the theorem is complete.

Next we shall consider the case where $\mathfrak{X}$ is treated as a linear lattice—the algebraic operations allowed including the linear operations as well as the two lattice operations. Here an ideal

is to be defined as a nonvoid class closed under the allowed
algebraic operations and enjoying the additional property that
it contains with f every g such that

$$|g(x)| \leqq |f(x)|$$

for all x. Our principal result concerning closed ideals is essentially due to Kakutani[2]; it follows from Theorem 3 much as
Theorem 6 follows from Theorem 2.

THEOREM 7: *Let $\mathfrak{X}$ be the linear lattice of all the continuous real
functions on a compact space X, let $\mathfrak{X}_0$ be an arbitrary nonvoid
subfamily of $\mathfrak{X}$, let X_0 be the closed set of all those points x at which
every function f in $\mathfrak{X}_0$ vanishes, and let $\mathfrak{Y}_0$ be the family of those
functions f in $\mathfrak{X}$ which vanish at every point of X_0. Then $\mathfrak{Y}_0$ is the
smallest closed ideal containing $\mathfrak{X}_0$; and $\mathfrak{X}_0$ is a closed ideal if and
only if $\mathfrak{X}_0 = \mathfrak{Y}_0$. A closed ideal $\mathfrak{X}_0$ is characterized by the associated
closed set X_0; in particular, $\mathfrak{X}_0 = \mathfrak{Y}_0 = \mathfrak{X}$ if and only if X_0 is void.*

Proof: It is evident that $\mathfrak{Y}_0$ is a closed ideal containing $\mathfrak{X}_0$.
For example, if f is in $\mathfrak{Y}_0$ and $|g(x)| \leqq |f(x)|$ for every x, then g
vanishes everywhere on X_0 and therefore belongs to $\mathfrak{Y}_0$. If $\mathfrak{X}_0$
is a closed ideal we can show that $\mathfrak{X}_0 = \mathfrak{Y}_0$. To do so we refer to
Theorem 3 and consider what linear relations of the form indi-
cated there can be satisfied by every function in $\mathfrak{X}_0$. Obviously
the pairs of points x, y which have one or both members in X_0
are of no further interest, as the corresponding linear conditions
are those of types (1) and (2), the effect of which has already
been taken into account through the introduction of the closed
set X_0. Turning to the case where x and y are distinct points not
in X_0, we first remark that if we have $f(x) = f(y)$ for every f in
$\mathfrak{X}$, then no *effective* restriction is implied by the linear relation
corresponding to the pair of points in question. Assuming therefore that g is a function in $\mathfrak{X}$ with $g(x) \neq g(y)$, we may suppose
without loss of generality that $g(x) = 1$, $g(y) = 0$—for we may
replace g if necessary by the function h defined through the
equation

$$h(z) = \frac{g(z) - g(y)}{g(x) - g(y)}$$

for all z in X. Since x is not in X_0 there is a function f in $\mathfrak{X}_0$ such that $f(x) \neq 0$. We may suppose without loss of generality that $f(x) > 1$ for we may replace f if necessary by the function $h = \alpha f$ with a suitable value of α. The function $h = |f| \cap |g|$ is now seen to be in the ideal $\mathfrak{X}_0$ and to satisfy the equations $h(x) = 1$, $h(y) = 0$. Accordingly, no linear relation of the type (3) or type (4) is satisfied by h. Hence the linear relations which characterize $\mathfrak{X}_0$ as a closed linear sublattice of $\mathfrak{X}$ reduce effectively to those implicit in the statement that every function in $\mathfrak{X}_0$ vanishes throughout X_0. It follows that $\mathfrak{X}_0 = \mathfrak{Y}_0$. Obviously if $\mathfrak{X}_0$ is an arbitrary nonvoid family and $\mathfrak{X}_1$ is a closed ideal containing $\mathfrak{X}_0$, then the associated closed set X_1 is part of X_0; and $\mathfrak{X}_1 = \mathfrak{Y}_1 \supset \mathfrak{Y}_0$. This completes the proof of the theorem.

Finally, we take up the case where $\mathfrak{X}$ is to be regarded as a (linear) ring—the algebraic operations considered being addition and multiplication (and multiplication by real constants). Here an ideal is a subset of $\mathfrak{X}$ which contains $f + g$ whenever it contains f and g, and which contains fg whenever it contains f. Since multiplication of f by the real number α is equivalent to multiplication of f by the constant function g everywhere equal to α, we see that an ideal automatically contains αf together with f. Our main result reads exactly like Theorem 7, differing from it only in the interpretation that has to be given to the term "ideal."

THEOREM 8: *Let $\mathfrak{X}$ be the linear ring of all the continuous real functions on a compact space X, let $\mathfrak{X}_0$ be an arbitrary nonvoid subfamily of $\mathfrak{X}$, let X_0 be the closed set of all those points x at which every function f in $\mathfrak{X}_0$ vanishes, and let $\mathfrak{Y}_0$ be the family of all those functions f in $\mathfrak{X}$ which vanish at every point of X_0. Then $\mathfrak{Y}_0$ is the smallest closed ideal containing $\mathfrak{X}_0$; and $\mathfrak{X}_0$ is a closed ideal if and only if $\mathfrak{X}_0 = \mathfrak{Y}_0$. A closed ideal $\mathfrak{X}_0$ is characterized by the associated closed set X_0; in particular, $\mathfrak{X}_0 = \mathfrak{Y}_0 = \mathfrak{X}$ if and only if $\mathfrak{X}_0$ is void.*

Proof: It is evident that $\mathfrak{Y}_0$ is a closed ideal containing $\mathfrak{X}_0$. For example, if f is in $\mathfrak{Y}_0$ and g is arbitrary, then fg vanishes throughout X_0 and is therefore a function in $\mathfrak{Y}_0$. If $\mathfrak{X}_0$ is a closed ideal, it is a closed linear subring. By using Theorem 5, we can show that $\mathfrak{X}_0 = \mathfrak{Y}_0$. The argument is much like that applied in the discussion of the analogous relation in Theorem 7. Since $\mathfrak{X}_0$ is characterized by the set X_0 and the linear relations of the form $g(x) = g(y)$ (where x and y are outside X_0) which are satisfied by every function in $\mathfrak{X}_0$, we have to eliminate the latter by appealing to the fact that $\mathfrak{X}_0$ is an ideal. If the condition $g(x) = g(y)$ is satisfied for *every* g in $\mathfrak{X}$, then there is no effective condition corresponding to the pair of points x, y. If there is some function g such that $g(x) \neq g(y)$, we may suppose that $g(x) = 1$, $g(y) = 0$. Since f can be found in $\mathfrak{X}_0$ so that $f(x) = 1$, the function $h = fg$ is in $\mathfrak{X}_0$ and $h(x) = 1$, $h(y) = 0$. Hence there is no condition of the form $g(x) = g(y)$ which is satisfied by all functions in $\mathfrak{X}_0$. This establishes the identity of $\mathfrak{X}_0$ and $\mathfrak{Y}_0$. The remainder of the discussion follows exactly the lines laid down in the proof of Theorem 7.

The connection between Theorems 7 and 8 is made plain by the following theorem.

THEOREM 9: *If $\mathfrak{X}$ is the family of all continuous real functions on a compact space X, then $\mathfrak{X}$ is both a linear lattice and a (linear) ring. A nonvoid closed subfamily $\mathfrak{X}_0$ of $\mathfrak{X}$ is a linear lattice ideal if and only if it is a ring ideal.*

Proof: The result follows immediately from a comparison of Theorems 7 and 8. It would also be possible to give a proof by direct examination of the ideal properties. Thus, if $\mathfrak{X}_0$ is a closed linear lattice ideal, we show it to be a ring ideal as follows. If f is in $\mathfrak{X}_0$ and g in $\mathfrak{X}$, then α can be found so that $|g(x)| \leq \alpha$ for every x—and it therefore follows that the product $h = fg$ satisfies the relations

$$|h(x)| = |f(x)g(x)| \leq |\alpha f(x)| = |(\alpha f)(x)|$$

and hence belongs to $\mathfrak{X}_0$ along with f and αf. On the other hand, if $\mathfrak{X}_0$ is a closed ring ideal, it is a closed sublattice by virtue of Theorem 4. In particular, $\mathfrak{X}_0$ contains $|f|$ together with f. Thus, if f is in $\mathfrak{X}_0$ and g is in $\mathfrak{X}$, the function h_n defined by putting

$$h_n(x) = \frac{|f(x)|g(x)}{|f(x)| + (1/n)}$$

for all x, is in $\mathfrak{X}_0$. If g satisfies theinequality $|g(x)| \leqq |f(x)|$ for every x, then

$$|g(x) - h_n(x)| \leqq \frac{|g(x)|}{n|f(x)| + 1} \leqq \frac{|f(x)|}{n|f(x)| + 1}$$

$$\leqq \frac{1}{n}\left(1 - \frac{1}{n|f(x)| + 1}\right) \leqq \frac{1}{n}.$$

Since the sequence h_n thus converges uniformly to g, we see that g is in $\mathfrak{X}_0$ also.

5. EXTENSION TO COMPLEX FUNCTIONS

It is natural to consider the extension of the preceding results to the case of complex-valued functions. The fact that the complex numbers are not ordered is an obstacle to the introduction of lattice operations for complex-valued functions. Accordingly, the results of Section 2 do not lend themselves to extension in the desired sense, unless they are first expressed in terms of the operation of forming the absolute value. However, it is easy to see that the complex-linear operations (addition and multiplication by complex numbers) and the operation of forming the absolute value do not work well enough together for us to obtain any very interesting or useful extension to the complex case.

Matters appear quite differently when we consider the linear-ring operations. In fact, we find here that extremely interesting new possibilities, quite beyond the scope of the present inquiry, are immediately opened up. For example, the theory of analytic functions can be considered as an answer to the question, "If X is a bounded closed subset of the complex plane, and $\mathfrak{X}_0$ is the family of all polynomials in the complex variable z, what functions can be uniformly approximated on X by functions in $\mathfrak{X}_0$?" As this observation clearly suggests, a full investigation of the complex case is both difficult and rewarding.[12] In order to limit ourselves to considerations of the kind already met in the preceding sections, we shall include the operation of forming conjugates along with the linear-ring operations in our examination of the complex case. Accordingly, if $\mathfrak{X}$ is the family of all bounded continuous complex-valued functions on a topological space X, and $\mathfrak{X}_0$ is an arbitrary subfamily of $\mathfrak{X}$, we designate by $\mathfrak{U}(\mathfrak{X}_0)$ the family of all those functions which can be obtained from $\mathfrak{X}_0$ by the linear-ring operations, the operation of forming conjugates, and uniform passages to the limit. It is easily seen that $\mathfrak{U}(\mathfrak{X}_0)$ is obtainable by using first the algebraic operations and then a single passage to the limit, and that $\mathfrak{U}(\mathfrak{X}_0)$ is closed under all the operations permitted. If we designate the conjugate by means of a bar, so that $\bar{f}$ is the function whose value $\bar{f}(x)$ at x is equal to the conjugate of the complex number $f(x)$, we can define two related operations, namely those of forming the real part and the imaginary part of f, by the equations

$$\Re f = \tfrac{1}{2}(f + \bar{f}), \qquad \Im f = \tfrac{1}{2}i(f - \bar{f})$$

from which the relations

$$f = \Re f + i\Im f, \qquad \bar{f} = \Re f - i\Im f$$

follow directly. The functions $\Re f$ and $\Im f$ are real-valued continuous functions which belong to $\mathfrak{U}(\mathfrak{X}_0)$ whenever f is in $\mathfrak{X}_0$. It is easy to see that $\mathfrak{U}(\mathfrak{X}_0)$ can be obtained in the following manner: We first form the family $\mathfrak{Y}_0$ of all real-valued functions expressible as $\Re f$ or $\Im f$ where f is in $\mathfrak{X}_0$; we then form the family $\mathfrak{B}(\mathfrak{Y}_0)$ of all those (real) functions which can be obtained from $\mathfrak{Y}_0$ by the real linear-ring operations and uniform passage to the limit; and finally we find $\mathfrak{U}(\mathfrak{X}_0)$ as the family of all functions $f + ig$ where f and g are in $\mathfrak{B}(\mathfrak{Y}_0)$. In view of this observation we can carry Theorem 5 and its corollaries over to the complex case without any further difficulty. The results will be given without further discussion, as follows:

THEOREM 10: *Let X be a compact space, $\mathfrak{X}$ the family of all continuous complex functions on X, $\mathfrak{X}_0$ an arbitrary subfamily of $\mathfrak{X}$, and $\mathfrak{U}(\mathfrak{X}_0)$ the family of all functions (necessarily continuous) generated from $\mathfrak{X}_0$ by the linear-ring operations, the operation of forming the conjugate, and uniform passage to the limit. Then a necessary and sufficient condition for a function f in $\mathfrak{X}$ to be in $\mathfrak{U}(\mathfrak{X}_0)$ is that f*

satisfy every linear relation of the form $g(x) = 0$ or $g(x) = g(y)$ which is satisfied by all functions in $\mathfrak{X}_0$. If $\mathfrak{X}_0$ is a closed linear subring of $\mathfrak{X}$ which contains $\bar{f}$ together with f—that is, if $\mathfrak{X}_0 = \mathfrak{U}(\mathfrak{X}_0)$—then $\mathfrak{X}_0$ is characterized by the system of all the linear relations of this kind which are satisfied by every function belonging to it. In other words, $\mathfrak{X}_0$ is characterized by the partition of X into mutually disjoint closed subsets on each of which every function in $\mathfrak{X}_0$ is constant and by the specification of that one, if any, of these subsets on which every function in $\mathfrak{X}_0$ vanishes.

COROLLARY 1: *In order that $\mathfrak{U}(\mathfrak{X}_0)$ contain a nonvanishing constant function, it is necessary and sufficient that for every x in X there exist some f in $\mathfrak{X}_0$ such that $f(x) \neq 0$.*

COROLLARY 2: *If $\mathfrak{X}_0$ is a separating family for X, then $\mathfrak{U}(\mathfrak{X}_0)$ either coincides with $\mathfrak{X}$ or is, for a uniquely determined point x_0, the family of all functions f in $\mathfrak{X}$ such that $f(x_0) = 0$. Conversely, if $\mathfrak{X}$ is a separating family for X and $\mathfrak{U}(\mathfrak{X}_0)$ either coincides with $\mathfrak{X}$ or is the family of all those f in $\mathfrak{X}$ which vanish at some fixed point x_0 in X, then $\mathfrak{X}_0$ is a separating family.*

In the case of complex-valued functions, the definition of an ideal remains the same: A nonvoid subclass $\mathfrak{X}_0$ of $\mathfrak{X}$ is said to be an ideal if $\mathfrak{X}_0$ contains $f + g$ whenever it contains both f and g, and $\mathfrak{X}_0$ contains fg whenever it contains f, g being an arbitrary function in $\mathfrak{X}$. Clearly, an ideal is closed under the linear-ring operations, since multiplication by a complex number is equivalent to multiplication by a constant complex-valued function. Now if an ideal $\mathfrak{X}_0$ is closed under uniform passages to the limit, we can show that $\mathfrak{X}_0$ contains $\bar{f}$ together with f. For an arbitrary function f in $\mathfrak{X}_0$, we define a function g_n by putting

$$g_n(x) = \overline{f(x)} |f(x)|^{1/n} / f(x)$$

when $f(x) \neq 0$ and $g_n(x) = 0$ when $f(x) = 0$. If x is any point in X and x_0 any point such that $f(x_0) = 0$ we have

$$|g_n(x)| = |f(x)|^{1/n}, \qquad |g_n(x) - g_n(x_0)| = |f(x) - f(x_0)|^{1/n},$$

whence g_n is bounded on X and continuous at x_0. On the other hand, it is evident that g_n is continuous at any point x where $f(x) \neq 0$. Thus g_n is a function in $\mathfrak{X}$ and fg_n a function in the ideal $\mathfrak{X}_0$. The function

$$h_n = |\bar{f} - fg_n| = |\bar{f}(1 - |f|^{1/n})| = ||f| - |f|^{1+1/n}|$$

is evidently a real continuous function on X which converges as $n \longrightarrow \infty$ to the function everywhere equal to zero. For any x it is easily verified that $h_n(x)$ is a nonincreasing sequence. Accordingly, Corollary 1 to Theorem 1 shows that the convergence is uniform. It follows that fg_n converges uniformly to $\bar{f}$ and hence that f is in the closed ideal $\mathfrak{X}_0$. As a result we can state without further preliminaries the following extension of Theorem 8 from the real to the complex case, essentially due to Shilov.

THEOREM 11:[3] *Let $\mathfrak{X}$ be the linear ring of all the continuous complex functions on a compact space X, let $\mathfrak{X}_0$ be an arbitrary nonvoid subfamily of $\mathfrak{X}$, let X_0 be the closed set of all those points x at which every function f in $\mathfrak{X}_0$ vanishes, and let $\mathfrak{Y}_0$ be the family of all those functions f in $\mathfrak{X}$ which vanish at every point of X_0. Then $\mathfrak{Y}_0$ is the smallest closed ideal containing $\mathfrak{X}_0$; and $\mathfrak{X}_0$ is a closed ideal if and only if $\mathfrak{X}_0 = \mathfrak{Y}_0$. A closed ideal $\mathfrak{X}_0$ is characterized by the associated closed set X_0; in particular, $\mathfrak{X}_0 = \mathfrak{Y}_0 = \mathfrak{X}$ if and only if X_0 is void.*

Proof: It is obvious that $\mathfrak{Y}_0$ is an ideal. If a closed ideal $\mathfrak{X}_1$ contains $\mathfrak{X}_0$, then by virtue of what we have just proved above, it is a linear subring which contains $\bar{f}$ along with f; and hence a simple argument based on Theorem 10 shows that $\mathfrak{X}_1$ contains $\mathfrak{Y}_0$. The remainder of the theorem follows then in a familiar way.

6. THE EXTENSION TO LOCALLY COMPACT SPACES

A natural question arises as to the possibility of relaxing the topological conditions imposed hitherto upon the space X. A thorough examination of this question would take us too far afield. Suffice it to say that a great deal of light can be thrown on this question by applying the theory of compactification developed by the writer[1] and by Čech in a later paper.[4] In fact, it can be said that this theory allows us to solve the problem of approximation in the family $\mathfrak{X}$ of all bounded continuous real (or complex) functions on an *arbitrary* topological space X—in exactly the same sense that the problem has been solved above for compact X. The essence of the method alluded to in these remarks is to replace X by a suitable compactification X^*, extending every function in $\mathfrak{X}$ over the compact space X^* without sacrifice of its continuity. There is, however, one very special instance of sufficient immediate interest for us to pay it some attention here. This is the case where X is a locally compact space.

By definition, a space is locally compact if every point of the space is interior to some compact subset of the space. Typical examples of spaces which are locally compact without being compact are afforded by the Euclidean spaces of n dimensions. If X is a locally compact space which is not compact, it can be compactified, as is well known, by the adjunction of a single point. Specifically, we adjoin an element x_∞ to X, obtaining the set X^*, and we define a subset U^* of X^* to be open if it is a subset of X and is open in X, or if it is the complement of a *closed* compact subset of X (note that, whereas a closed subset of a compact space is compact, a compact subset of a topological space is not necessarily closed unless it is a Hausdorff space!). The totality of open sets in X^* is easily verified to have the properties normally required: X^* and its void subset are open; the union of any family of open sets is open; and the intersection of any finite family of open sets is open. Moreover, X^* can be shown to be compact, as follows: In any family of open sets whose union is X^* we can find one open set containing x_∞; its complement X_0 is compact and is contained in the union of the remaining open sets in the family; but then a finite number of the latter must, because X_0 is compact, have a union containing X_0.

In order that a real function f defined on X should agree there with a function f^* defined and continuous on X^*, it is necessary and sufficient that the function f, in addition to being continuous on X, should satisfy the inequality

$$|f(x) - f(y)| < \epsilon$$

for all x and y outside a suitable closed compact set X_ϵ. The necessity of the condition is obvious: When f^* exists, there is an open set U_ϵ^* containing x_∞ such that for all x and y in it

$$|f^*(x) - f^*(x_\infty)| < \epsilon/2, \qquad |f^*(y) - f^*(x_\infty)| < \epsilon/2,$$

and hence

$$|f(x) - f(y)| = |f^*(x) - f^*(y)| < \epsilon;$$

the appropriate set X_ϵ is therefore the complement of U_ϵ^*. The sufficiency of the condition is easy to prove aside from the determination of the value which should be assigned to f^* at x_∞. Let Z be the closure of the set of all real numbers $\zeta = f(x)$, where x is in X and is restricted to lie in a fixed open subset of X^* containing x_∞. Since X is not compact, the intersection of any finite number of such open sets must contain points of X, and the corresponding sets Z therefore have a common point. Thus any finite number of the sets Z will have a common point. There exists a set Z of diameter not exceeding an arbitrarily prescribed positive number ϵ, since we may determine a set X_ϵ in accordance with the assumed condition and may take Z as the set corresponding to the open set complementary to X_ϵ: the relation

$$|f(x) - f(y)| < \epsilon$$

for all x and y outside X_ϵ implies that the diameter of Z does not exceed ϵ. Any such set Z, being closed and bounded, is compact. Hence there exists a unique real number ζ_∞ common to all the sets Z. We now put $f^*(x) = f(x)$ for x in X and $f^*(x_\infty) = \zeta_\infty$. Obviously, the function so defined is continuous at every point of X. To show that it is continuous at x_∞, we prescribe $\epsilon > 0$ arbitrarily, determine a corresponding set $X_{\epsilon/2}$ by virtue of the assumed condition, and take Z as the set associated with the open set $U_{\epsilon/2}^*$ complementary to $X_{\epsilon/2}$. Obviously there is a point y in $U_{\epsilon/2}^*$ and in X such that

$$|f(y) - \zeta_\infty| < \epsilon/2;$$

and at the same time $|f(x) - f(y)| < \epsilon$ for all x in $U_{\epsilon/2}^*$ and in X. Consequently f^* is continuous at x_∞, as we desired to show.

Since the extension of a function f satisfying the given condition is uniquely determined, it is clear that the study of the continuous functions on X which do satisfy the condition is equivalent to the study of the continuous functions on X^*. Hence if we denote the totality of such functions as $\mathfrak{X}$ and totality of their extensions by $\mathfrak{X}^*$, the approximation theorems in $\mathfrak{X}$ are translatable into approximation theorems in $\mathfrak{X}^*$ and vice versa. In making the indicated translation it is frequently convenient to have a characterization of those functions in $\mathfrak{X}$ which vanish at x_∞ in the sense that $f^*(x_\infty) = 0$. It is easily seen, as a matter of fact, that the property in question is equivalent to the following property: corresponding to $\epsilon > 0$ there is a closed compact subset X_ϵ of X such that $|f(x)| < \epsilon$ for all x outside X. The totality of such functions is obviously a closed linear lattice ideal and a closed ring ideal in $\mathfrak{X}$, as we see by directly applying the results of Section 4 to $\mathfrak{X}^*$. We shall designate this class of functions as $\mathfrak{X}_\infty$. One of the most useful and typical approximation theorems for a locally compact, but not compact, space X is then stated as follows:

THEOREM 12: *Let X be a locally compact, but not compact, space, and let $\mathfrak{X}$ and $\mathfrak{X}_\infty$ have the significance indicated above. If $\mathfrak{X}_0$ is any subfamily of $\mathfrak{X}_\infty$, which is a separating family for X and which contains for any x_0 in X a function f_0 such that $f_0(x_0) \neq 0$, then any function in $\mathfrak{X}_\infty$ can be uniformly approximated by linear lattice polynomials or by ordinary polynomials in members of $\mathfrak{X}_0$; and any function in $\mathfrak{X}$ can be similarly approximated by functions which result from the addition of a fixed constant function to such polynomials.*

Proof: If we look at $\mathfrak{X}^*$ and $\mathfrak{X}_\infty^*$, we see that $\mathfrak{X}_0^*$ is a separating family for X^* and that every function f^* in it vanishes at x_∞, $f^*(x_\infty) = 0$. By Theorems 3 and 7 we see that every function in $\mathfrak{X}_\infty^*$ can be uniformly approximated by linear lattice polynomials in members of $\mathfrak{X}_0^*$. Similarly, by Corollary 2 to Theorem 5 we obtain the corresponding statement for ordinary polynomials. If these results are now put in terms of $\mathfrak{X}$, $\mathfrak{X}_\infty$, and $\mathfrak{X}_0$, we obtain the present theorem. If f is in $\mathfrak{X}$, then we see that the function g, defined by putting $g(x) = f(x) - f^*(x_\infty)$ for every x, is in $\mathfrak{X}_\infty$ since

$$g^*(x_\infty) = f^*(x_\infty) - f^*(x_\infty) = 0.$$

Since g can be uniformly approximated by linear lattice polynomials or ordinary polynomials in members of $\mathfrak{X}_0$, we conclude that f can be approximated by functions obtained by adding a constant function (everywhere equal to $f^*(x_\infty)$) to such a polynomial.

A useful special instance of this theorem may be phrased as follows:

COROLLARY 1: *Let X be a locally compact, but not compact, Hausdorff space; and let $\mathfrak{X}_0$ be a family of real continuous functions on X with the following properties: each function in $\mathfrak{X}_0$ vanishes outside a corresponding compact subset of X; corresponding to any point x_0 in X and any open set U which contains x_0 is a function in $\mathfrak{X}_0$ vanishing outside U and assuming at x_0 a value different from 0. Then $\mathfrak{X}_0$ has all the properties listed in the theorem above.*

Proof: Since any compact subset of X is now necessarily closed, it is evident that $\mathfrak{X}_0$ is part of $\mathfrak{X}_\infty$. It is easily verified that $\mathfrak{X}_0$ is a separating family for X, since when x_0 and x_0' are distinct points in X there is an open set U containing x_0 but not x_0' and hence a function f_0 in $\mathfrak{X}_0$ vanishing outside U and not vanishing at x_0, whence

$$f_0(x_0) \neq f_0(x_0') = 0.$$

We now see that $\mathfrak{X}_0$ satisfies the requirements laid down in Theorem 12, and the corollary is established.

For the case of complex-valued functions, all the preceding remarks can evidently be repeated almost verbatim; the only essential changes are to suppress all references to lattice properties and to require of $\mathfrak{X}_0$ in Theorem 12 and the corollary that it contain $\bar{f}$ along with f. No further comment on this case would seem necessary.

7. THE LEBESGUE-URYSOHN EXTENSION THEOREM

As a first application of the approximation theorems developed in the preceding sections, we shall discuss a variant of the celebrated and important Lebesgue-Urysohn extension theorem, which asserts that corresponding to any continuous real function defined on a closed subset X_0 of a normal space X there exists a continuous real function defined on the entire space X and agreeing throughout X_0 with the given function. Since the known proofs of this theorem are quite simple (see, for example, Alexandroff-Hopf[5]), the present discussion is chiefly of interest in the realm of systematics. It would take us too far afield, in any event, to prove the extension theorem in its full generality, since the method to be applied consists in first compactifying the normal space X and then applying the results which we shall establish below. We shall therefore postpone the presentation of the full proof to some other occasion. Here we shall consider the case where X_0 is compact and X arbitrary, obtaining a result which in some respects actually goes beyond that summarized above as the Lebesgue-Urysohn extension theorem. We confine ourselves to the case of real functions, since the complex case is an essentially trivial consequence of it. Accordingly the theorem to be proved here can be stated as follows:

THEOREM 13: *Let X be an arbitrary topological space, X_0 a compact subset of X, f_0 a continuous function defined on X_0, and $\mathfrak{X}_0$ a family of continuous real functions defined on X with the following properties: $\mathfrak{X}_0$ is closed under the linear lattice [linear-ring] operations; $\mathfrak{X}_0$ is closed under uniform passage to the limit; $\mathfrak{X}_0$ contains all constant functions. In the case of the linear-ring operations, let $\mathfrak{X}_0$ have further the property (verified automatically in the linear lattice case) that whenever it contains a function f it also contains a function g which coincides with f on X_0 and has the same bounds on X as f does on X_0. Then for f_0 to be extensible in $\mathfrak{X}_0$, in the sense that there exists a function f in $\mathfrak{X}_0$ agreeing with f_0 throughout X_0, it is necessary and sufficient that f_0 satisfy every linear condition of the form*

$$f(x_0) = f(y_0), \qquad x_0 \neq y_0, \qquad x_0 \in X_0, \qquad y_0 \in X_0,$$

which is satisfied by every member of $\mathfrak{X}_0$. The extension f can be so chosen as to have the same bounds on X as f_0 has on X_0.

Proof: We first remark that the application of the linear lattice [linear-ring] operations to extensible functions defined on X_0 produces extensible functions, since $\mathfrak{X}_0$ is assumed to be a linear lattice [linear-ring]. We then observe that the uniform limit on X_0 of extensible functions is extensible. Indeed, let a sequence of functions g_n in $\mathfrak{X}_0$ converge uniformly on X_0 to a limit function g_0 (defined on X_0). We may suppose (by thinning out the originally given sequence, should that be necessary) that

$$|g_{n+1}(x) - g_n(x)| \leqq 2^{-n}$$

for every x in X_0. We then take h_n to be an extension of $g_{n+1} - g_n$ such that $|h_n| \leqq 2^{-n}$. This is always possible, since we can choose h_n as a member of $\mathfrak{X}_0$ which has on X the same bounds as does $g_{n+1} - g_n$ on X_0; or, in the linear lattice case, we can simply take h_n so that

$$h_n(x) = \max \ \min \ (g_{n+1}(x) - g_n(x), 2^{-n}, -2^{-n}).$$

Now the series

$$g_1 + \sum_{n=1}^{\infty} h_n$$

converges uniformly to a continuous real function g in $\mathfrak{X}_0$ which agrees on X_0 with g_0. The family of all extensible functions on X_0 thus constitutes a closed linear sublattice [linear subring] of the linear lattice [linear ring] of all continuous real functions on X_0, and includes the constant functions on X_0. Theorem 3 and its corollary in the lattice case and Theorem 5 and its Corollary 1 in the ring case show that the family of all extensible functions on X_0 coincides with the family of all those continuous functions on X_0 which satisfy every linear condition of the form

$$f(x_0) = f(y_0), \qquad x_0 \neq y_0, \qquad x_0 \in X_0, \qquad y_0 \in Y_0,$$

which is satisfied by every function in $\mathfrak{X}_0$. The final statement of the theorem is obvious. In the lattice case, if α and β are the greatest lower and least upper bounds of f_0 on X_0 (both finite because X_0 is compact) and if f is any extension of f_0 in $\mathfrak{X}_0$, then f can be replaced by g where

$$g(x) = \max\,(\min\,(f(x),\,\beta),\,\alpha).$$

The most interesting case of Theorem 13 is that in which $\mathfrak{X}_0$ is taken to be the family of all continuous functions on X. For this case we may state Theorem 13 in the following form.

COROLLARY 1: *In order that a continuous real function f_0 defined on a compact subset X_0 of a topological space X have a continuous extension defined over X, it is necessary and sufficient that f_0 satisfy every condition of the form*

$$f(x_0) = f(y_0), \qquad x_0 \neq y_0, \qquad x_0 \in X_0, \qquad y_0 \in Y_0$$

which is satisfied by all continuous functions on X—in other words, that f_0 be constant on every subset of X_0 where all the functions continuous on X are constant by virtue of the topological structure of X. In particular, this condition is superfluous when the continuous functions on X constitute a separating family for X_0: every real function continuous on X_0 then has a continuous extension defined on X. If a function f_0 on X_0 has a continuous extension on X, then it has such an extension with the same bounds on X as f_0 has on X_0.

8. THE THEOREM OF DIEUDONNÉ

A second interesting and useful application, still in the field of general topology, can now be made to a situation first adequately discussed by Dieudonné. Here we must presuppose the rudiments of the theory of the cartesian product of topological spaces. It is convenient to think of the product of the spaces X_α (where α runs over a fixed index-set A) as a coordinate space, each point x being specified by its coordinates x_α in the respective factor spaces X_α. Now if α is a fixed index and f_α is a continuous real function defined on the factor space X_α, we can define a continuous real function f on the product space by putting $f(x) = f_\alpha(x_\alpha)$ where x_α is the coordinate of x corresponding to the index α. Such a function f will be called here a function of one variable—specifically, the function of one variable associated with f_α. These simple preliminaries enable us to state our main result as follows:

THEOREM 14:[6] *If X is the cartesian product of compact spaces X_α, $\alpha \in A$, then every continuous real function on X can be uniformly approximated by finite sums of finite products of continuous functions of one variable on X.*

Proof: The cartesian product of compact spaces is known to be compact. Let now $\mathfrak{X}_0$ be the totality of those functions expressible as finite sums of finite products of continuous functions of one variable on X. Since the sums, products, and constant multiples of functions in $\mathfrak{X}_0$ are obviously also in $\mathfrak{X}_0$, we see that $\mathfrak{X}_0$ is a linear subring of the ring $\mathfrak{X}$ of all continuous real functions on X. Obviously $\mathfrak{X}_0$ contains all the constant functions. In order to be able to apply the results of Section 3 we therefore have to determine what linear relations of the form $f(x) = f(x')$ where $x \neq x'$ are satisfied by every function f in $\mathfrak{X}_0$. Since we may take f here as the function of one variable associated with an arbitrary continuous real function f_α on X_α, we must evidently have $f_\alpha(x_\alpha) = f_\alpha(x'_\alpha)$ for all f_α. Conversely, if x and x' are points such that $f_\alpha(x_\alpha) = f_\alpha(x'_\alpha)$ for every continuous real function f_α on X_α and for all α, then it is evident that $f(x) = f(x')$ for every f in $\mathfrak{X}_0$. Hence we see that any function in $\mathfrak{X}$ which satisfies all the linear relations of the above type can be uniformly approximated by functions in $\mathfrak{X}_0$, by virtue of Theorem 5. We can therefore complete our proof by showing that any continuous real function on X satisfies all these conditions.

First let us consider two points x and x' such that for some fixed index β we have $x_\beta \neq x'_\beta$ while $x_\alpha = x'_\alpha$ for all $\alpha \neq \beta$. From any function f on X, we can obtain a function f_β on X_β by putting $f_\beta(y_\beta) = f(y)$ where y_β is arbitrary and

$$y_\alpha = x_\alpha = x'_\alpha$$

for $\alpha \neq \beta$; and f_β is continuous when f is. Hence we see that if x_β and x'_β are points such that

$$f_\beta(x_\beta) = f_\beta(x'_\beta)$$

for every continuous real function f_β on X_β, then

$$f(x) = f_\beta(x_\beta) = f_\beta(x'_\beta) = f(x').$$

Let us suppose that when we have generalized the result just established and have proved that, when x and x' are two points such that for fixed indices $\beta_1, \cdots, \beta_n$ we have

$$f_{\beta_k}(x_{\beta_k}) = f_{\beta_k}(x'_{\beta_k})$$

for every continuous real function f_{β_k} on X_{β_k}, $k = 1, \cdots, n$ while $x_\alpha = x'_\alpha$ for every α other than $\beta_1, \cdots, \beta_n$, then $f(x) = f(x')$ for every f in $\mathfrak{X}$. We can then establish the corresponding result for points differing in at most $n + 1$ coordinates. In fact, let x and x' be given so that

$$f_{\beta_k}(x_{\beta_k}) = f_{\beta_k}(x'_{\beta_k})$$

as above for $k = 1, \cdots, n + 1$ while $x_\alpha = x'_\alpha$ for all α other than $\beta_1, \cdots, \beta_{n+1}$. We define a point x'' by putting $x''_{\beta_k} = x_{\beta_k}$ for $k = 1, \cdots, n$, $x''_{\beta_{n+1}} = x'_{\beta_{n+1}}$ for $k = n + 1$, and $x''_\alpha = x_\alpha = x'_\alpha$ for all α other than $\beta_1, \cdots, \beta_{n+1}$. It is obvious then that $f(x) = f(x'')$ for every f in $\mathfrak{X}$ by the result explicitly proved above. On the other hand, the assumption we have made implies that $f(x') = f(x'')$ for every f in $\mathfrak{X}$. Hence we conclude that $f(x) = f(x')$ for every f in $\mathfrak{X}$ as we wished to show. By induction, therefore, we conclude that if two points x and x' differ only in respect to their coordinates for a finite number of indices for each of which $f_\beta(x_\beta) = f(x'_\beta)$ for every continuous real function f_β on X_β, then $f(x) = f(x')$ for all f in $\mathfrak{X}$.

Finally, let us suppose that f is in $\mathfrak{X}$ and that x and x' are points such that for every α and every continuous real function f_α on X_α the relation $f_\alpha(x_\alpha) = f_\alpha(x'_\alpha)$ holds. Then we can determine for any positive ϵ a neighborhood U_ϵ of x such that

$$|f(x) - f(y)| < \epsilon$$

for every y in U_ϵ by virtue of the continuity of f. By the way in which the topology of X is defined, we can now determine a point x'' which is in U_ϵ and which nevertheless differs from x' only in respect to a finite number of coordinates. This end can indeed be achieved by designating appropriate indices $\beta_1, \cdots, \beta_n$ and putting $x''_{\beta_k} = x_{\beta_k}$ for $k = 1, \cdots, n$ while

$x_\alpha'' = x_\alpha'$ for all other indices α. We then have $f(x'') = f(x')$ in accordance with our previous results and hence also

$$|f(x) - f(x')| = |f(x) - f(x'')| < \epsilon.$$

Since ϵ is arbitrary, we conclude that $f(x) = f(x')$, whatever the function f in $\mathfrak{X}$.

Useful variants of this theorem can be obtained by considering the case where some of the factor spaces are locally compact but not compact. As they would involve us in more extensive topological discussions than seem desirable here, we shall leave the matter at this point.

It will be useful, perhaps, to recall a classical application of the theorem just proved: In the theory of integral equations a standard procedure is to replace the kernel $K(x, y)$, assumed to be a continuous function of its arguments on the square

$$a \leqq x \leqq b, \qquad a \leqq y \leqq b,$$

by a uniformly good approximant of the form

$$K'(x, y) = F_1(x)G_1(y) + \cdots + F_n(x)G_n(y)$$

where $F_1, \cdots, F_n$ and $G_1, \cdots, G_n$ are continuous functions on the interval $[a, b]$. Since the square is the cartesian product of the intervals

$$a \leqq x \leqq b, \qquad a \leqq y \leqq b,$$

the theorem of Dieudonné gives a direct justification for this device.

9. THE WEIERSTRASS APPROXIMATION THEOREM

In the present section we propose to derive from the results of Section 3 a demonstration of the classical Weierstrass approximation theorem. Although we shall give a comparatively broad version of the theorem, everything we shall have to say is merely a direct specialization of previously established results to the case at hand. The steps of the general development which would have to be retained in a direct independent proof of the Weierstrass theorem will be indicated after the derivation of the theorem from Section 3 has been presented.

THEOREM 15:[7] *Let X be an arbitrary bounded closed subset of n-dimensional cartesian space, the coordinates of a general point being $x_1, \cdots, x_n$. Any continuous real function f defined on X can be uniformly approximated on X by polynomials in the variables $x_1, \cdots, x_n$. In case X contains the origin $x = (0, \cdots, 0)$, the function f can be uniformly approximated by polynomials vanishing at the origin if and only if f itself vanishes at the origin. Otherwise f can be uniformly approximated by such polynomials without qualification.*

Proof: The functions $f_1, \cdots, f_n$, where $f_k(x) = x_k$, are continuous real functions of x. They constitute a separating family $\mathfrak{X}_0$ for X since $x = x'$ if and only if

$$x_k = f_k(x) = f_k(x') = x_k'$$

for $k = 1, \cdots, n$. When X does not contain the origin, then we cannot have

$$f_1(x) = f_n(x) = 0$$

for any x in X; but when X contains the origin we obtain

$$f_1(x) = \cdots = f_n(x) = 0$$

by taking x as the origin. Since X is bounded and closed, it is compact. Accordingly, the results of Section 3, especially those stated in Corollary 2 to Theorem 5, show that any continuous real function f on X can be uniformly approximated by functions of the form (where $\alpha_1, \cdots, \alpha_n$ are positive integers or 0)

$$p(x) = \sum_{1 \leq \alpha_1 + \cdots + \alpha_n \leq N} C_{\alpha_1 \ldots \alpha_n}(f_1(x))^{\alpha_1} \cdots (f_n(x))^{\alpha_n}$$

$$= \sum_{1 \leq \alpha_1 + \cdots + \alpha_n \leq N} C_{\alpha_1 \ldots \alpha_n} x_1^{\alpha_1} \cdots x_n^{\alpha_n},$$

with the proviso that when X contains the origin, f must vanish there. If the constant function everywhere equal to 1 is adjoined to the family $\mathfrak{X}_0$, we see that f can be uniformly approximated on

X by functions of the form

$$p(x) = \sum_{0 \leq \alpha_1 + \cdots + \alpha_n \leq N} C_{\alpha_1 \ldots \alpha_n} x_1^{\alpha_1} \cdots x_n^{\alpha_n}.$$

This completes the proof.

If one wishes to give a direct proof of the Weierstrass approximation theorem by the present methods, the following procedure is available. It is best to consider first the family $\mathfrak{X}_0$ of all homogeneous linear functions l, where

$$l(x) = c_1 x_1 + \cdots + c_n x_n,$$

noting that for any given continuous real function f on X (provided f vanishes at the origin when this point is in X) a function l can be found so that $l(x) = f(x)$, $l(y) = f(y)$ at arbitrarily prescribed points x, y in X. Considerations like those used in the proof of Theorem 1 show that such a function f can be uniformly approximated by lattice combinations of functions in $\mathfrak{X}_0$. Theorem 4 has to be established exactly as in Section 3. It can then be used to convert approximation by lattice combinations into approximation by linear-ring combinations of functions in $\mathfrak{X}_0$, just as was done in the proof of Theorem 5. The main part of the proof is thereby completed. Remarks similar to those above have to be added concerning the adjunction of constant functions to $\mathfrak{X}_0$.

10. TRIGONOMETRIC APPROXIMATION

A surprisingly direct and simple application of Theorem 5 yields the fundamental theorem on trigonometric approximation in the real domain, reading as follows.

THEOREM 16: *Let f be an arbitrary continuous real function of the real variable* θ, $0 \leq \theta \leq 2\pi$, *subject to the periodicity condition* $f(0) = f(2\pi)$. *Then f can be uniformly approximated on its domain of definition by trigonometric polynomials—that is, by functions of the form*

$$p(\theta) = \frac{a_0}{2} + \sum_{n=1}^{N} (a_n \cos n\theta + b_n \sin n\theta).$$

Proof: It is convenient to make the application of Theorem 5 directly to the case of the unit circle X (given by the equation $x_1^2 + x_2^2 = 1$) in the cartesian plane, thus obtaining a special instance of the Weierstrass approximation theorem as stated in Theorem 15. If we rephrase this special case in terms of the central angle θ corresponding to a general point x on the circle X, we see that the functions continuous on the circle are the functions continuous and periodic in θ and that the polynomials in x_1 and x_2 (in terms of which such functions can be uniformly approximated) are functions of the form

$$p(\theta) = \sum_{1 \leq m+n \leq N} c_{mn} \cos^m \theta \sin^n \theta$$

since $x_1 = \cos \theta$ and $x_2 = \sin \theta$.

The addition formulas for the trigonometric functions yield the relations

$$2 \cos m\theta \cos n\theta = \cos (m + n)\theta + \cos (m - n)\theta$$
$$2 \cos m\theta \sin n\theta = \sin (m + n)\theta + \sin (m - n)\theta$$
$$2 \sin m\theta \sin n\theta = -\cos (m + n)\theta + \cos (m - n)\theta$$

which enable us to establish by a recursive argument that $\cos^m \theta \sin^n \theta$ (and hence also every function of the form $p(\theta)$ described above) is a trigonometric polynomial in the sense required by the statement of the theorem. Indeed, we have only to note that, if $\cos^m \theta \sin^n \theta$ is such a polynomial, then $\cos^{m+1} \theta \sin^n \theta$ and $\cos^m \theta \sin^{n+1} \theta$ are also trigonometric polynomials by virtue of the indicated relations.

The complex form of the trigonometric approximation theorem can be deduced even more readily from Theorem 10, Corollary 2; it can be stated as follows:

Theorem 17: *If f is a continuous complex function of the real variable θ, $0 \leq \theta \leq 2\pi$ subject to the periodicity condition $f(0) = f(2\pi)$, then f can be uniformly approximated by functions p of the form*

$$p(\theta) = \sum_{n = -N}^{n = +N} C_n e^{ni\theta},$$

where the constants C_n are complex numbers.

Proof: The functions considered will be treated as continuous functions on the unit circle X, θ being the central angle as in the discussion of the preceding theorem. Since

$$e^{mi\theta}e^{ni\theta} = e^{(m+n)i\theta} \quad \text{and} \quad \overline{e^{ni\theta}} = e^{-ni\theta},$$

it is clear that the family $\mathfrak{X}_0$ of all functions p of the form

$$p(\theta) = \sum_{n=-N}^{n=+N} C_n e^{ni\theta}$$

is a linear subring of the family $\mathfrak{X}$ of all continuous complex functions on X, the function $\bar{p}$ being in $\mathfrak{X}_0$ whenever p is. It is also evident that the functions $e^{ni\theta}$ satisfy no linear relation of the form $e^{ni\theta_0} = 0$ or of the form $e^{ni\theta_1} = e^{ni\theta_2}$, $\theta_1 \neq \theta_2$, where $0 \leqq \theta_1 < 2\pi$, $0 \leqq \theta_2 < 2\pi$. Consequently, every function in $\mathfrak{X}$ can be uniformly approximated by functions in $\mathfrak{X}_0$, in accordance with Corollary 2 to Theorem 10. This completes the proof.

11. APPROXIMATION BY LAGUERRE FUNCTIONS

An important problem of analysis concerns the approximation of real functions continuous on the half-infinite interval $0 \leqq x < +\infty$ by linear combinations of the functions $e^{-\alpha x}x^n$, $n = 0, 1, 2, \cdots$, where α is a fixed positive number. In order to obtain a solution to this problem within the scope of the present discussion, we need a lemma concerning the exponential function.

LEMMA 1: *On the interval $0 \leqq x < \infty$ the function e^{-nx}, where n is a positive integer and $\alpha > 0$, can be uniformly approximated by functions of the form $e^{-\alpha x}p(x)$ where p is a polynomial.*

Proof: We may suppose without loss of generality that $\alpha = 1$. Indeed if for $\epsilon < 0$ we have found a polynomial $q(x)$ such that

$$\left| e^{-nx} - e^{-x}q(x) \right| < \epsilon$$

for $0 \leqq x < \infty$, we can replace x by αx and $q(x)$ by the polynomial $p(x) = q(\alpha x)$, obtaining

$$\left| e^{-n\alpha x} - e^{-\alpha x}p(x) \right| < \epsilon$$

for $0 \leqq x < \infty$. We shall now proceed recursively. When $n = 1$

there is nothing to prove, since e^{-x} is already of the form specified for its approximants. When $n = 2$, we obtain the desired result by estimating the magnitude of the function f where

$$f(x) = e^{-2x} - e^{-x} \sum_{k=0}^{N} \frac{(-x)^k}{k!}.$$

Since f is continuous and has the properties $f(0) = 0$ and $\lim_{x \to \infty} f(x) = 0$, it has an extremum on the interval $0 < x < \infty$. If such an extremum occurs at $x = x_0$, then

$$0 = f'(x_0) = -2e^{-2x_0} + 2e^{-x_0} \sum_{k=0}^{N-1} \frac{(-x)^k}{k!} + e^{-x_0} \frac{(-x_0)^N}{N!}$$

so that

$$f(x_0) = \frac{1}{2} e^{-x_0} \frac{(-x_0)^N}{N!}.$$

Consequently, we have

$$\sup_{0 \le x < \infty} |f(x)| \le \frac{1}{2N!} \sup_{0 \le x < \infty} e^{-x} x^N.$$

For $N \ge 1$ the function g defined by putting $g(x) = e^{-x} x^N$ is continuous and nonnegative on the interval $0 \le x < \infty$ and has the properties $g(0) = 0$, $\lim_{x \to \infty} g(x) = 0$. It therefore has a maximum on the interval $0 < x < \infty$, occurring at the only solution there of the equation

$$0 = g'(x) = e^{-x}(N - x) x^{N-1}$$

—that is, at $x = N$. Accordingly we have $0 \le g(x) \le e^{-N} N^N$. Applying so much of Stirling's formula as is necessary to show that

$$N! \le e^{-N} N^{N+1/2}/2K$$

for a suitable constant $K > 0$, we obtain the inequality

$$|f(x)| \le K N^{-1/2}.$$

The case $n = 2$ is thereby settled.

If we have proved the lemma for any particular positive integer n, we can discuss the approximation of $e^{-(n+1)x}$ in the following manner. If $\epsilon > 0$ is given, we first use what is known about the approximation of $e^{-2\alpha x}$, taking $2\alpha = n + 1$, so as to obtain a polynomial q such that

$$\left| e^{-(n+1)x} - e^{-nx/2-x/2}q(x) \right| < \tfrac{1}{2}\epsilon.$$

The function $e^{-x/2}|q(x)|$ is bounded on the interval $0 \leqq x < \infty$. If its least upper bound is A, we use what is known about the approximation of $e^{-n\alpha x}$, taking $\alpha = \tfrac{1}{2}$, so as to obtain a polynomial r such that

$$\left| e^{-nx/2} - e^{-x/2}r(x) \right| < \frac{\epsilon}{2A}.$$

It follows that

$$\left| e^{-nx/2-x/2}q(x) - e^{-x}q(x)r(x) \right| < e^{-x/2}|q(x)|\frac{\epsilon}{2A} \leqq \frac{1}{2}\epsilon$$

and

$$\left| e^{-(n+1)x} - e^{-x}p(x) \right| < \epsilon,$$

where $p = qr$. Mathematical induction therefore serves to complete the proof of the lemma.

A direct application of Theorem 12 together with the lemma just proved yields the main approximation theorem of this section.

THEOREM 18: *Any continuous real function f, which is defined on the interval $0 \leqq x < \infty$ and vanishes at infinity in the sense that* $\lim_{x\to\infty} f(x) = 0$, *can be uniformly approximated by functions of the form $e^{-\alpha x}p(x)$ where $p(x)$ is a polynomial.*

Proof: We let X be the interval $0 \leqq x < \infty$. As a topological space, X is locally compact. The function $e^{-\alpha x}$ is in $\mathfrak{X}_\infty$ since $\lim_{x\to 0} e^{-\alpha x} = 0$. We now let $\mathfrak{X}_0$ consist of this function alone. It is obvious from the monotonicity of the exponential function that $\mathfrak{X}_0$ is a separating family for X. Moreover, there is no $x \geqq 0$ for which $e^{-\alpha x} = 0$. By hypothesis the function f to be approximated is in $\mathfrak{X}_\infty$. Theorem 12 thus shows that f can be uniformly approximated on X by functions of the form

$$\sum_{n=1}^{N} C_n e^{-n\alpha x}.$$

Lemma 1 then yields the present theorem.

A variant of the above proof can be based on a direct appeal to the Weierstrass approximation theorem. We introduce a new variable $\xi = e^{-\alpha x}$, $0 < \xi \leqq 1$. The function ϕ defined by putting

$$\phi(0) = 0, \qquad \phi(\xi) = f(x) = f\left(\frac{-1}{\alpha} \log \xi\right)$$

is continuous on the interval $0 \leqq \xi \leqq 1$. Hence ϕ can be uniformly approximated by polynomials

$$\sum_{n=1}^{N} C_n \xi^n,$$

and f can be uniformly approximated by functions of the form

$$\sum_{n=1}^{N} C_n e^{-n\alpha\xi}.$$

Lemma 1 is then used to complete the proof.

It is of some interest to apply the approximation theorem just proved to derive results concerning approximation in the mean. The classical theorem on this subject reads as follows:

THEOREM 19: *The functions of the form $e^{-\alpha x}p(x)$ where $p(x)$ is a polynomial are dense in the function space $L_r(0, \infty)$, $r \geqq 1$.*

Proof: Here $L_r(0, \infty)$ is the class of all real Lebesgue-measurable functions f on the interval $0 \leqq x < \infty$ for which the Lebesgue integral

$$\int_0^\infty |f(x)|^r \, dx$$

exists. The expression

$$\left(\int_0^\infty |f(x)|^r \, dx\right)^{1/r}$$

is taken as the norm of f, and $L_r(0, \infty)$ then becomes a complete normed linear vector space. It is obvious that every function of the form $e^{-\alpha x}p(x)$, where p is a polynomial, is a member of $L_r(0, \infty)$. We wish to prove that if $\epsilon > 0$ and if f is in $L_r(0, \infty)$, then there exists a function of this special form for which

$$\left(\int_0^\infty |f(x) - e^{-\alpha x}p(x)|^r \, dx\right)^{1/r} < \epsilon.$$

It is well known that there exists a function g, continuous on the interval $0 \leq x < \infty$ and vanishing outside some bounded interval, for which

$$\left(\int_0^\infty |f(x) - g(x)|^r \, dx \right)^{1/r} < \frac{1}{2} \epsilon.$$

We therefore need only show that it is possible to find a function of the indicated special form for which

$$\left(\int_0^\infty |g(x) - e^{-\alpha x} p(x)|^r \right)^{1/r} < \frac{1}{2} \epsilon.$$

The function $e^{(1/2)\alpha x} g(x)$ is continuous on $0 \leq x < \infty$ and vanishes outside some bounded interval. Hence we can find a polynomial $p(x)$ such that

$$\left| e^{(1/2)\alpha x} g(x) - e^{-(1/2)\alpha x} p(x) \right| < \eta$$

where $\eta < \frac{1}{2}(r\alpha/2)^{1/r}\epsilon$. Accordingly, we obtain the relations

$$\left(\int_0^\infty |g(x) - e^{-\alpha x} p(x)|^r \right)^{1/r}$$

$$= \left(\int_0^\infty |e^{(1/2)\alpha x} g(x) - e^{-(1/2)\alpha x} p(x)|^r \, e^{-r\alpha x/2} \, dx \right)^{1/r}$$

$$\leq \eta \left(\int_0^\infty e^{-r\alpha x/2} \, dx \right)^{1/r} = \left(\frac{2}{r\alpha} \right)^{1/r} \eta < \frac{1}{2} \epsilon.$$

The proof is thereby completed.

A useful related theorem is the following:

THEOREM 20: *If f is in $L_r(0, \infty)$, $r \geq 1$, or if f is a bounded Lebesgue-measurable function, then the integrals*

$$\int_0^\infty f(x) e^{-\alpha x} x^n \, dx$$

exist for $\alpha > 0$ and $n = 0, 1, 2, \cdots$. If these integrals vanish for fixed α and $n = 0, 1, 2, \cdots$, then $f(x)$ vanishes almost everywhere.

Proof: When f is in $L_1(0, \infty)$, the fact that the functions $e^{-\alpha x}x^n$ are bounded yields the existence of the integrals in question. When f is in $L_r(0, \infty)$ for $r > 1$, the fact that the functions $e^{-\alpha x}x^n$ are in $L_{r'}(0, \infty)$ where $1/r + 1/r' = 1$, yields a like result in the standard way. Finally, when f is bounded and Lebesgue-measurable, it is the fact that the functions $e^{-\alpha x}x^n$ are in $L_1(0, \infty)$ which yields the desired result. Using this result, we see that in every case the function

$$g(x) = e^{-(1/4)\alpha x} \int_0^x f(t)e^{-(1/4)\alpha t}\, dt$$

is a continuous function with the property that

$$|g(x)| \leq Ke^{-(1/4)\alpha x}$$

for some constant K. Thus g is in $L_2(0, \infty)$. Moreover an integration by parts shows that

$$\int_0^\infty g(x)e^{-(1/2)\alpha x}x^n\, dx = \int_0^\infty \left(\int_0^x f(t)e^{-(1/4)\alpha t}\, dt \right) (e^{-(3/4)\alpha x}x^n)\, dx$$

$$= \int_0^\infty (f(x)e^{-(1/4)\alpha x}) \left(\int_0^x e^{-(3/4)\alpha t}t^n\, dt \right) dx$$

$$= \int_0^\infty f(x)e^{-\alpha x}p(x)\, dx = 0$$

since

$$\int_0^x e^{-(3/4)\alpha t}t^n\, dt = e^{-(3/4)\alpha x}p(x)$$

where $p(x)$ is a polynomial and since it is assumed that

$$\int_0^\infty f(x)e^{-\alpha x}x^n\, dx = 0$$

for $n = 0, 1, 2, \cdots$. We have thus reduced the proof of the theorem to the special case where the given function is in $L_2(0, \infty)$. Choosing a polynomial $p(x)$ such that

$$\left(\int_0^\infty |g(x) - e^{-(1/2)\alpha x}p(x)|^2\, dx \right)^{1/2} < \epsilon$$

and noting that

$$\int_0^\infty g(x)e^{-(1/2)\alpha x}p(x)\, dx = 0,$$

we have

$$\int_0^\infty |g(x)|^2\, dx = \int_0^\infty (g(x) - e^{-(1/2)\alpha x}p(x))g(x)\, dx$$

$$\leqq \left(\int_0^\infty |g(x) - e^{-(1/2)\alpha x}p(x)|^2\, dx\right)^{1/2}$$

$$\left(\int_0^\infty |g(x)|^2\, dx\right)^{1/2}$$

by Schwarz's inequality; and we therefore have

$$\left(\int_0^\infty |g(x)|^2\, dx\right)^{1/2} < \epsilon.$$

It follows that

$$\int_0^\infty |g(x)|^2\, dx = 0$$

and that $g(x)$, being continuous, vanishes identically. The relation

$$\int_0^x f(t)e^{-(1/4)\alpha t}\, dt = 0$$

is thus established. From this it follows that

$$f(x)e^{-(1/4)\alpha x} = 0 \quad \text{and} \quad f(x) = 0,$$

almost everywhere.

In the three theorems proved in this section, it is obvious that the hypotheses concerning the function f can be altered to allow f to be complex, without changing the conclusions.

12. APPROXIMATION BY HERMITE FUNCTIONS

The methods of the preceding section can be applied with little modification to yield comparable results concerning uniform approximation by linear combinations of the functions $e^{-\alpha^2 x^2}x^n$ on the full infinite interval $-\infty < x < +\infty$. Using Theorem 12 and Lemma 1, we immediately obtain the chief result.

THEOREM 21: *Any continuous real function f which is defined on the interval $-\infty < x < +\infty$ and which vanishes at infinity in the sense that*

$$\lim_{x \to -\infty} f(x) = \lim_{x \to +\infty} f(x) = 0$$

can be uniformly approximated by functions of the form $e^{-\alpha^2x^2}p(x)$
where $p(x)$ *is a polynomial.*

Proof: We let X be the interval $-\infty < x < +\infty$. As a topological space, X is locally compact. The functions f, $e^{-\alpha^2x^2}$, and $e^{-\alpha^2x^2}x$ are in $\mathfrak{X}_\infty$, since they all vanish at infinity in the sense indicated in the statement of the theorem. The family $\mathfrak{X}_0$, consisting of the two functions $e^{-\alpha^2x^2}$, $e^{-\alpha^2x^2}x$, is obviously a separating family for X; moreover, there is no x for which $e^{-\alpha^2x^2} = 0$. Theorem 12 thus shows that f can be uniformly approximated by functions of the form

$$\sum_{m=1}^{M} \sum_{n=1}^{N} c_{mn}e^{-m\alpha^2x^2}x^n.$$

To complete the discussion, we make use of Lemma 1. Letting A be the maximum of the function $e^{-(1/2)\alpha^2x^2}|x|^n$, we find a polynomial q such that

$$\left|e^{-(2m-1)t} - e^{-t}q(t)\right| < \frac{\epsilon}{A}$$

for $0 \leq t < \infty$. We now put $t = \frac{1}{2}\alpha^2x^2$, multiply both sides of the inequality by

$$e^{-(1/2)\alpha^2x^2}|x|^n,$$

and write $p(x)$ for $x^nq(\frac{1}{2}\alpha^2x^2)$, obtaining

$$\left|e^{-m\alpha^2x^2}x^n - e^{-\alpha^2x^2}p(x)\right| < e^{-(1/2)\alpha^2x^2}|x|^n\epsilon/A \leq \epsilon.$$

The theorem then follows.

A variant of this proof can be given by appropriate use of the Weierstrass approximation theorem, as stated in Section 9. We introduce a variable point ξ of the cartesian plane with the coordinates $x_1 = e^{-\alpha^2x^2}$, $x_2 = e^{-\alpha^2x^2}x$. The locus of this point ξ, with the origin adjoined, provides a bounded closed set X in the plane. The function ϕ defined by putting $\phi(\xi) = f(x)$ when

$$\xi = (x_1, x_2) = (e^{-\alpha^2x^2}, e^{-\alpha^2x^2}x)$$

and $\phi(\xi) = 0$ when ξ is the origin is a continuous function of ξ on X. The Weierstrass approximation theorem shows that ϕ can be uniformly approximated on X by a polynomial

$$\sum_{l=1}^{L} \sum_{n=1}^{N} c'_{ln} x_1^l x_2^n.$$

Hence f can be uniformly approximated on the interval $-\infty < x < +\infty$ by a function of the form

$$\sum_{l=1}^{L} \sum_{n=1}^{N} c'_{ln} e^{-(l+n)\alpha^2 x^2} x^n = \sum_{m=1}^{M} \sum_{n=1}^{N} c_{mn} e^{-m\alpha^2 x^2} x^n,$$

where $m = l + n$, $M = L + N$, and $c_{mn} = c'_{m-n,n}$. The remainder of the proof is identical with that given above.

By a method almost the same as that used in proving Theorem 19, we obtain the corresponding result for approximation in the mean by functions of the form $e^{-\alpha^2 x^2} p(x)$ where p is a polynomial. The theorem is therefore stated without detailed proof.

THEOREM 22: *The functions of the form $e^{-\alpha^2 x^2} p(x)$, where $p(x)$ is a polynomial, are dense in the function space $L_r(-\infty, +\infty)$, $r \geqq 1$.*

By using the results of Theorem 20 we can give a simple proof of its analogue for the functions $e^{-\alpha^2 x^2} x^n$.

THEOREM 23: *If f is in $L_r(-\infty, +\infty)$, $r \geqq 1$, or if f is a bounded Lebesgue-measurable function, then the integrals*

$$\int_{-\infty}^{+\infty} f(x) e^{-\alpha^2 x^2} x^n \, dx$$

exist for $\alpha > 0$ and $n = 0, 1, 2, \cdots$. If these integrals vanish for fixed α and $n = 0, 1, 2, \cdots$, then $f(x)$ vanishes almost everywhere.

Proof: Let f_1 and f_2 be the functions defined by putting

$$2f_1(x) = f(x) + f(-x), \qquad 2f_2(x) = f(x) - f(-x),$$

so that f_1 is even, f_2 is odd, and $f = f_1 + f_2$. It is evident that f_1 and f_2 are in $L_r(-\infty, +\infty)$ when f is, and are bounded when f is. We easily see that

$$2 \int_0^\infty f_2(x) e^{-\alpha^2 x^2} x^{2m+1} \, dx = \int_{-\infty}^{+\infty} f_2(x) e^{-\alpha^2 x^2} x^{2m+1} \, dx$$

$$= \int_{-\infty}^{+\infty} f(x) e^{-\alpha^2 x^2} x^{2m+1} \, dx = 0.$$

The function f_2, considered on the half-infinite interval $0 \leqq x < \infty$, is in $L_r(0, \infty)$ or is bounded according to whether f_2 is in $\mathcal{L}_r(-\infty, +\infty)$ or is bounded. We now make the change of variable $t = x^2$ and write

$$g(t) = f_2(x)e^{-(1/2)\alpha^2 x^2},$$

obtaining

$$\int_0^\infty g(t)e^{-(1/2)\alpha^2 t}t^m \, dt = 2\int_0^\infty f_2(x)e^{-\alpha^2 x^2}x^{2m+1} \, dx = 0,$$

$$\int_0^\infty |g(t)|^r \, dt = 2\int_0^\infty |f_2(x)|^r e^{-(r/2)\alpha^2 x^2}x \, dx < +\infty,$$

so that g is in $L_r(0, \infty)$ if f is and is bounded if f is. Thus Theorem 20 is applicable and yields the result that $g(x)$ vanishes almost everywhere. It follows that f is essentially an even function of x, the equation $f(-x) = f(x)$ being satisfied almost everywhere. It is easy to see that the function h defined by putting

$$h(x) = f(x)e^{-(1/2)\alpha^2 x^2}x$$

is essentially odd; that h is in $L_r(-\infty, +\infty)$ when f is and is bounded when f is; and that

$$\int_{-\infty}^{+\infty} h(x)e^{-(1/2)\alpha^2 x^2}x^n \, dx = 0$$

for $n = 0, 1, 2, \cdots$. By what has already been proved, h must be essentially even. However, since it was given as an essentially odd function, it must vanish almost everywhere. Thus $f(x) = 0$ almost everywhere, as we wished to prove.

It is obvious that in the three theorems proved in this section the hypotheses concerning the function f can be altered so as to allow f to be complex without changing the conclusions.

13. THE PETER-WEYL APPROXIMATION THEOREM

As a final application of our results concerning approximation, we shall sketch briefly a proof of the theorem of Peter and Weyl concerning the approximation of functions on a compact topological group. (The proof offered here was presented by the author to a seminar held at the University of Buenos Aires in 1943.) This theorem includes as a special case the classical theorems on trigonometric approximation given in Section 10, as is well known.

Let X be a compact topological group. It is known that this group has a complete system of mutually inequivalent, irreducible continuous real (respectively, complex) matrix representations by finite orthogonal (respectively, unitary) matrices. Specifically, a system of finite orthogonal (respectively, unitary) matrices $\Lambda^{(k)}(x)$, where x is in X and $k = 1, 2, 3, \cdots$, can be found with the following properties:

1. *the elements of $\Lambda^{(k)}(x)$ depend continuously on x, the relation*

$$\Lambda^{(k)}(x)\Lambda^{(k)}(y) = \Lambda^{(k)}(xy)$$

   is satisfied, and $\Lambda^{(k)}(e)$, e being the identity element of X, is a unit matrix;

2. *the continuous representation of X given by $\Lambda^{(k)}(x)$ is irreducible;*

3. *the continuous representations of X given by $\Lambda^{(k)}(x)$ and $\Lambda^{(k')}(x)$ are inequivalent when $k \neq k'$;*

4. *any irreducible continuous real (respectively, complex) matrix representation of X is equivalent to the representation given by $\Lambda^{(k)}(x)$ for some k (necessarily unique);*

5. *any two distinct elements x and y of the group X determine at least one k such that*

$$\Lambda^{(k)}(x) \neq \Lambda^{(k)}(y).$$

The problem to be discussed is that of approximating a general continuous function on X in terms of the functions $\lambda_{ij}^{(k)}$ defined by taking $\lambda_{ij}^{(k)}(x)$ as the element standing in the ith row and jth column of the matrix $\Lambda^{(k)}(x)$. We shall therefore take $\mathfrak{X}$ to be the family of all continuous real (respectively, complex) functions on X, and $\mathfrak{X}_0$ as the family comprising all the functions $\lambda_{ij}^{(k)}$, $i = 1, \cdots, n_k, j = 1, \cdots, n_k, k = 1, 2, 3, \cdots$. By virtue of (1) we see that $\mathfrak{X}_0$ is part of $\mathfrak{X}$. By virtue of (5) we see that $\mathfrak{X}_0$ is a separating family for X. A trivial irreducible representation of X can be obtained by letting $\Lambda(x)$ be the matrix of one row and one column whose single element has the value 1. From (1) and (4) we must have $\Lambda(x) = \Lambda^{(k)}(x)$ for some k, necessarily unique. Hence $\mathfrak{X}_0$ contains the constant function which assumes the value 1 everywhere on X. In the complex case, it is evident that the matrix $\overline{\Lambda^{(k)}(x)}$ whose elements are the conjugates of the elements of $\Lambda^{(k)}(x)$ gives an irreducible unitary representation of X, by virtue of the relation

$$\overline{\Lambda^{(k)}(x)\Lambda^{(k)}(y)} = \overline{\Lambda^{(k)}(xy)}.$$

Because of (4) this representation is equivalent to that given by the matrices $\Lambda^{(k')}(x)$ for some k, necessarily unique. Thus there is a nonsingular constant matrix Λ such that

$$\overline{\Lambda^{(k)}(x)} = \Lambda^{-1}\Lambda^{(k')}(x)\Lambda.$$

Accordingly, each of the functions $\overline{\lambda_{ij}^{(k)}}$ is a linear combination (with constant coefficients) of the functions $\lambda_{i'j'}^{(k')}$, $i' = 1, \cdots,$ n'_k, $j' = 1, \cdots, n'_k$. The most important property of all is expressed by a similar statement—namely, that the product $\lambda_{ij}^{(k)}\lambda_{i'j'}^{(k')}$ is a finite linear combination with real (respectively, complex) constant coefficients of the functions $\lambda_{i''j''}^{(k'')}$. The proof of this assertion is obtained by considering the representation of X given by the Kronecker product

$$\Lambda^{(k)}(x) \times \Lambda^{(k')}(x)$$

of the matrices $\Lambda^{(k)}(x)$ and $\Lambda^{(k')}(x)$. The Kronecker product in question is a matrix of $n_k^2 n_{k'}^2$ elements whose rows and columns are labeled by the pairs (i, i'), (j, j') respectively, the element standing in the row labeled (i, i') and column labeled (j, j') being

$$\lambda_{ij}^{(k)}(x)\lambda_{i'j'}^{(k')}(x).$$

By direct computation it is easy to verify that

$$(\Lambda^{(k)}(x) \times \Lambda^{(k')}(x))(\Lambda^{(k)}(y) \times \Lambda^{(k')}(y))$$
$$= (\Lambda^{(k)}(x)\Lambda^{(k)}(y)) \times (\Lambda^{(k')}(x)\Lambda^{(k')}(y)) = \Lambda^{(k)}(xy) \times \Lambda^{(k')}(xy).$$

Hence the Kronecker product provides a continuous representation of X. When this representation is resolved into its irreducible constituents, finite in number, each of the latter is equivalent in accordance with (4) to a representation $\Lambda^{(k'')}(x)$ for some k'', necessarily unique. This resolution corresponds to the determination of a matrix Λ of real (respectively, complex) constants such that the matrices

$$\Lambda(\Lambda^{(k)}(x) \times \Lambda^{(k')}(x))\Lambda^{-1} = \Lambda(x)$$

have the form indicated schematically as follows:

$$
\begin{bmatrix}
\Lambda^{(k_1'')}(x) & 0 & 0 & 0 \\
0 & \Lambda^{(k_2'')}(x) & 0 & 0 \\
0 & 0 & & 0 \\
0 & 0 & 0 & \Lambda^{(k_n'')}(x)
\end{bmatrix}
$$

Here the blocks along the principal diagonal are occupied by various ones of the matrices $\Lambda^{(k'')}(x)$ (not necessarily distinct!), and all other blocks are filled with zeros. The fact that

$$\Lambda^{(k)}(x)\Lambda^{(k')}(x) = \Lambda^{-1}\Lambda(x)\Lambda$$

leads at once to the conclusion that $\lambda_{ij}^{(k)}\lambda_{i'j'}^{(k')}$ is a real (respectively, complex) linear combination (with constant coefficients) of functions $\lambda_{i''j''}^{(k'')}$ corresponding to elements of the diagonal blocks in the matrix $\Lambda(x)$.

From the properties enumerated above we can now obtain the approximation theorem by direct applications of Theorems 5 and 10.

THEOREM 24 :[8] *Any continuous real (respectively, complex) function on the compact topological group X can be uniformly approximated on X by real (respectively, complex) linear combinations of the functions $\lambda_{ij}^{(k)}$ described above in terms of the irreducible representations of X.*

Proof: Let $\mathfrak{U}(\mathfrak{X}_0)$ be the family of all the real (respectively, complex) continuous functions on X which can be uniformly approximated by polynomials in members of $\mathfrak{X}_0$, the family of all the functions $\lambda_{ik}^{(k)}$. In view of the facts about the products $\lambda_{ij}^{(k)}\lambda_{i'j'}^{(k'')}$, it is clear that $\mathfrak{U}(\mathfrak{X}_0)$ is also the family of all the real (respectively, complex) continuous functions on X which can be uniformly approximated by real (respectively, complex) linear combinations of the functions $\lambda_{ij}^{(k)}$. In the complex case, we know further that $\mathfrak{U}(\mathfrak{X}_0)$ contains $\bar{f}$ along with f. Since $\mathfrak{X}_0$ is a separating family for X and contains nonvanishing constant functions, Theorem 5 shows that $\mathfrak{U}(\mathfrak{X}_0) = \mathfrak{X}$ in the real case, and Theorem 10 leads to the same result in the complex case.

14. LINEAR COMBINATIONS OF PRESCRIBED FUNCTIONS

It would be natural to study, by way of further generalizing the results obtained here, the problem of approximation in terms of linear combinations of prescribed functions. In this domain, however, are encountered some of the most difficult problems of analysis. For example, Wiener[9] has shown that general Tauberian theorems are intimately related to the problem of approximation in the mean by linear combinations of functions f_α obtained from a single function f in $L_1(-\infty, +\infty)$ by putting $f_\alpha(x) = f(x - \alpha)$. The conditions under which every function in $L_1(-\infty, +\infty)$ can be approximated in the mean (of order one) by such linear combinations were obtained by Wiener with the use of ingenious and powerful methods. Modern versions of his treatment have brought many simplifications, but nevertheless leave the impression that the results are among the deeper achievements of analysis.

In general, therefore, one cannot expect that the theory of this broader problem will assume so satisfactory a form as that which has been worked out when the lattice or the ring operations could be used to build approximants. The fact that in Sections 10–13 we were able to apply our theory to obtain results concerning particular cases of the broader problem is simply due to the observation that under certain circumstances it is possible to approximate products of the prescribed functions by linear combinations of them. This observation leads to an application of the ring theorems given in Sections 3 and 5, in the manner exemplified in Sections 10–13. Whenever a special theorem concerning the approximation of products by linear combinations can be established, the way is open for the employment of the same device.

REFERENCES

1. Stone, M. H., *Transactions of the American Mathematical Society*, Vol. 41 (1937), pp. 375–481, especially pp. 453–81.

2. Kakutani, Shizuo, *Annals of Mathematics*, Vol. 42 (1941), pp. 994–1024, especially pp. 1004–1005.

3. Shilov, G., *Comptes rendus (Doklady) de l'académie des sciences de l'U.R.S.S.*, Vol. 22 (1939), pp. 7–10.

4. Čech, E., *Annals of Mathematics*, Vol. 38 (1937), pp. 823–44.

5. Alexandroff, P., and H. Hopf, *Topologie I*. (Berlin, 1935), pp. 73–78.

6. Dieudonné, J., *Comptes rendus de l'académie des sciences*, Vol. 205 (1937), p. 593.

7. Weierstrass, Karl, *Mathematische Werke, Band 3, Abhandlungen III*, pp. 1–37, especially p. 5 (= *Sitzungsberichte der königlichen preussischen Akademie der Wissenschaften*, July 9 and July 30, 1885).

8. Peter, F., and H. Weyl, *Mathematische Annalen*, Vol. 97 (1927), pp. 737–55, especially p. 753.

9. Weiner, Norbert, *The Fourier Integral*. Cambridge: Cambridge University Press, 1933. See especially Chap. 2, Section 14.

ADDITIONAL READING

It would take an equally lengthy list to present an up-to-date picture of the results in algebraic analysis that have stemmed from the approximation theorem. We have therefore chosen to list only a few papers, selected because of their direct contact with Professor Stone's article.

Reference 11 is cited because it has an extensive bibliography, reaching into other aspects of the approximation theorem.

10. Buck, R. C., "Bounded continuous functions on a locally compact space," *Michigan Mathematics Journal*, Vol. 5 (1958), pp. 95–104.

11. ———, *On Numerical Approximation*. Madison: University of Wisconsin Press, 1959, pp. 341–69.

12. Mergelyan, S. N., "Uniform approximations of functions of a complex variable," *Uspehki matematičeski Nauk* (N.S.), Vol. 7, no. 2 (48), 1952, pp. 31–122.

13. Pollard, Harry, "The Bernstein approximation theorem," *Proceedings of the American Mathematical Society*, Vol. 6 (1955), pp. 402–11.

14. Rudin, Walter, "Subalgebras of spaces of continuous functions," *Proceedings of the American Mathematical Society*, Vol. 7 (1956), pp. 825–30.

15. Wermer, John, "Polynomial approximation on an arc in C^3," *Annals of Mathematics*, Vol. 62 (1955), pp. 269–70.

16. Whitney, Hassler, "On ideals of differentiable functions," *American Journal of Mathematics*, Vol. 70 (1948), pp. 635–58.

THE SPECTRAL THEOREM

Edgar R. Lorch

1. PRELIMINARY EXAMPLE

Before considering a logical or chronological exposition of the spectral theorem and of its meaning in analysis, it may be worthwhile examining a very simple example of it in ordinary three-dimensional euclidean space. We shall represent the points of this space by triplets (λ, μ, ν) of real numbers. We consider a transformation (that is, a map or function) H of the space into itself, for which we can therefore write

$$H(\lambda, \mu, \nu) = (\eta, \theta, \kappa).$$

Throughout this entire work, we shall assume that H is *linear*. This very vital concept will now be defined.

Let us use the symbol x to stand for the triplet (λ, μ, ν). If we have many triplets, we may denote them by x, y, x', and so on. Each triplet x may be considered a *vector;* one may, if one wishes, represent it by an arrow originating at the origin $(0, 0, 0)$ of three-space and terminating at the point (λ, μ, ν). For these vectors, there are defined two particularly simple operations which interest us here, namely, magnification by a real factor α and addition in accordance with the parallelogram law. These operations are usually called *scalar multiplication* and *vector addition*. In our notation we have the following relations:

If we denote the magnification of x by the real number α (which may be negative!) by αx, then

$$\alpha x = (\alpha\lambda, \; \alpha\mu, \; \alpha\nu).$$

If we denote the vector sum of x and x' by $x + x'$, and if $x' = (\lambda', \mu', \nu')$ then the three coordinates of $x + x'$ are:

$$\lambda + \lambda', \qquad \mu + \mu', \qquad \nu + \nu'.$$

A simple diagram in the plane will make these operations transparent.

Let us return to the concept of linearity for the transformation H. This is now easily explained. First let us agree that we may write the value of H on the vector x indiscriminately by Hx or $H(x)$. In particular, the symbols Hx, $H(x + x')$, $H(\alpha x)$ denote the values of H on x, $x + x'$, and αx, respectively. We recall that since Hx and Hx' are vectors, so are αHx and $Hx + Hx'$. The transformation H is said to be linear if and only if for all x, x', and α,

(1) $$H(\alpha x) = \alpha Hx,$$

(2) $$H(x + x') = Hx + Hx'.$$

There is a close relation between the theory of matrices and the theory of linear transformations. Incidentally, many of the misunderstandings that arise here are due to the fact that younger students frequently consider the two notions to be equivalent. This is not so. However, for finite-dimensional spaces, every linear transformation may be described by means of a matrix providing we have a *basis* of vectors for the given space of operations.

In euclidean three-space, the vectors $e_1 = (1, 0, 0)$, $e_2 = (0, 1, 0)$, and $e_3 = (0, 0, 1)$ play a special role. One important property they have is that each vector $x = (\lambda, \mu, \nu)$ can be expressed linearly in terms of them. For example, for the vector $x = (\lambda, \mu, \nu)$, we have

(3) $$x = \lambda e_1 + \mu e_2 + \nu e_3.$$

In fact, this representation is unique. These two properties of e_1, e_2, e_3 are described by the word *basis*. Note that there are many bases in three-space. Our initial description of the vectors in the space is peculiar in that we seem in advance to choose a basis, $\{e_1, e_2, e_3\}$, and then to consider all linear combinations of its elements. Notice another fact—e_1, e_2, e_3 are perpendicular to each other, which arises from the euclidean structure which we assumed at the start. In a euclidean space, there is a notion of angle, and in particular, of orthogonality.

Now, given any linear transformation H in three-space, its behavior is fully determined if it is known on e_1, e_2, and e_3. Indeed, we have

(4) $$Hx = \lambda He_1 + \mu He_2 + \nu He_3.$$

Each of the vectors He_1, He_2, He_3 has three components or coordinates. Thus the nature of H is completely determined by $3^2 = 9$ numbers which are usually written in a very special way in a square array called a *matrix*. If we let i stand for 1, 2, or 3 and set

$$He_i = \eta_{1i}e_1 + \eta_{2i}e_2 + \eta_{3i}e_3,$$

that is, He_i is the vector $(\eta_{1i}, \eta_{2i}, \eta_{3i})$, then the numbers η_{ij}, where $i = 1, 2, 3$ and $j = 1, 2, 3$, represent the transformation H. We have therefore associated to H and to the basis e_1, e_2, e_3 the matrix whose elements are η_{ij}. We write the association below:

(5) $$H \longrightarrow (\eta_{ij}).$$

We note that with respect to another basis, the matrix associated to H would (undoubtedly) be different. This consideration leads to a fundamental problem of transformation theory: *Given a transformation H, determine those bases in which the associated matrix is "simple."* The problem as yet has little precise meaning since we do not know how "simple" is to be interpreted. We shall get some insight into the various facets of simplicity if we turn at this stage to another and a very classic problem of transformation theory, the so-called *eigenvalue* problem.

The word *eigenvalue*, which undoubtedly gives both stylistic purists and some others considerable pain (which may well be justified and which we as a companionly gesture of good will are willing to share), is evidence of the profound influence which the German school has exercised on transformation theory. Other terms are *characteristic value* or, if one prefers, *eigenwert*. At any rate, an eigenvalue of H is a real number α such that there is a vector x which is not the *zero vector*, $(0, 0, 0)$, for which

$$(6) \qquad\qquad Hx = \alpha x.$$

If x is a nonzero vector satisfying (5), then x is called an *eigenvector* corresponding to the eigenvalue α. There may be many eigenvectors which correspond to a given eigenvalue. We note in passing that if x is the zero vector, then $Hx = \alpha x$ for every real number α. The eigenvalue problem is this: *For a given H, find all eigenvalues α and their associated eigenvectors.*

Let us solve the eigenvalue problem for two special transformations. Suppose O represents the zero transformation which maps every vector into the zero vector $0 = (0, 0, 0)$: $Ox = 0$ for each x. Then O is obviously linear. Its only eigenvalue is the real number 0, and each vector x is an eigenvector. Now let I represent the identity transformation defined by $Ix = x$ for each x. Then I is linear; the only eigenvalue is $\alpha = 1$, and each x is an eigenvector corresponding to that eigenvalue.

Let us consider one more example. Suppose H is defined as follows: $He_1 = e_1$, $He_2 = e_2$, $He_3 = 0$. Since H is linear, this information fixes H for all x. It is not difficult to see that 1 and 0 are the only eigenvalues; that the eigenvectors corresponding to the value 1 are of the form $(\lambda, \mu, 0)$; and that those corresponding to the value 0 are of the form $(0, 0, \nu)$. Thus, if $x = (\lambda, \mu, \nu)$,

$$Hx = (\lambda, \mu, 0) \quad \text{and} \quad H(\lambda, \mu, 0) = (\lambda, \mu, 0).$$

This means that for any vector x, $Hx = H(Hx)$. We usually write this in the form $H^2x = Hx$, or, better yet, $H^2 = H$. Transformations H for which $H^2 = H$ play a very important role in the discussion that follows.

Let us return to the general problem on the structure of linear transformations: Given a transformation H, determine those bases for which the associated matrix is as simple as possible; better and more broadly stated, determine those bases which reveal most information concerning the structure of H. At this stage of our discussion, it is clear that the solution of the eigenvalue problem is the first step in the solution of the more general problem. In some cases, the solution of the eigenvalue problem gives a complete clue to the structure problem. This is the case, for instance, if a transformation H in euclidean three-space has three distinct eigenvalues α_1, α_2, α_3; it is easy to show that if x_1, x_2, x_3 are any associated eigenvectors, they form a basis. A little later we shall explain the manner in which H acts in this case by introducing the notion of subspaces.

The eigenvalue problem in three-space is easily solved. For α to be an eigenvalue of the transformation H whose matrix is (η_{ij}), it is necessary and sufficient that there be solutions λ_1, λ_2, λ_3 not all zero of the system of homogeneous equations

$$(7) \qquad \sum_{j=1}^{3} (\eta_{ij} - \alpha\delta_{ij})\lambda_j = 0, \qquad i = 1, 2, 3.$$

Here, (δ_{ij}) is the matrix of the identity transformation—$\delta_{ij} = 0$ if $i \neq j$; $\delta_{ij} = 1$ if $i = j$. Note that Eq. (7) can be easily checked as follows: α is an eigenvalue corresponding to the vector $x = (\lambda_1, \lambda_2, \lambda_3)$ if and only if $Hx = \alpha Ix$, that is, if and only if the corresponding matrix equation (7) holds.

Equation (7) is readily solved. We first obtain the value of α by solving the determinant equation $|\eta_{ij} - \alpha\delta_{ij}| = 0$. This cubic in α has three roots, at least one of which is real. For each root, the associated λ_j can then be found by the theory of linear equations.

At this stage we see that the eigenwert problem in n-space will lead to the solution of an nth-degree equation. In order to obtain the maximum amount of information, we shall admit complex as well as real roots. The eigenvectors whose coordinates are the λ_i in Eq. (7) are then also complex. This leads us to assume that our space consists of all vectors x whose coordinates are complex. Admittedly, this introduces difficulties with respect to the geometry of our vector space. We shall see later how the euclidean character of the space can be preserved, leading to the notion of complex euclidean spaces. In the meantime, we shall assume henceforth that the coordinates of our vectors may be complex.

Let us return to three-dimensional euclidean space (which is now complex) and to the significance for this space of the spectral theorem. The spectral theorem is concerned with the structure of linear transformations. However, the center of interest lies in a certain type of linear transformation which is called *symmetric*. The precise definition of *symmetric transformation* will be given later when we consider the most general space in which the transformation acts. For the time being, it is sufficient to say that H is symmetric if and only if the matrix (η_{ij})—which, incidentally, now consists of complex numbers—has the property $\eta_{ji} = \bar{\eta}_{ij}$ where $\bar{\lambda}$ denotes the complex conjugate of λ.

The spectral theorem for this very simple example states that

1. *All eigenvalues of H are real.*

2. *If x and x' are eigenvectors belonging to distinct eigenvalues α and α', then x is orthogonal to x'.*

3. *It is possible to choose three vectors x_1, x_2, x_3 which are orthogonal each to each and such that each is an eigenvector.*

Let us look into the proof of these assertions. Let α be an eigenvalue of H; hence we have the equations in (7). In Eq. (7) multiply the ith equation by $\bar{\lambda}_i$ and add. We see that (definition of δ_{ij}!)

$$\sum_{i=1}^{3} \sum_{j=1}^{3} \delta_{ij}\lambda_j\bar{\lambda}_i = |\lambda_1|^2 + |\lambda_2|^2 + |\lambda_3|^2 > 0.$$

Also, $\sum_{i=1}^{3} \sum_{j=1}^{3} \eta_{ij}\lambda_j\bar{\lambda}_i$ is a real quantity, as follows by taking its complex conjugate and applying the fact that $\bar{\eta}_{ij} = \eta_{ji}$ since H is symmetric. It follows that α is real.

Towards the proof of property 2, we write

$$x = (\lambda_1, \lambda_2, \lambda_3) \quad \text{and} \quad x' = (\lambda_1', \lambda_2', \lambda_3').$$

We define the orthogonality of x and x' for complex spaces by the equality:

$$\lambda_1 \bar{\lambda}_1' + \lambda_2 \bar{\lambda}_2' + \lambda_3 \bar{\lambda}_3' = 0.$$

This certainly agrees with the usual definition for real vectors. Now, given that $\alpha \neq \alpha'$, $Hx = \alpha x$, $Hx' = \alpha' x'$, we have:

$$\sum_{i=1}^{3} \sum_{j=1}^{3} \eta_{ij} \lambda_j \bar{\lambda}_i' = \alpha \sum_{i=1}^{3} \lambda_i \bar{\lambda}_i',$$

$$\sum_{i=1}^{3} \sum_{j=1}^{3} \eta_{ij} \lambda_j' \bar{\lambda}_i = \alpha' \sum_{i=1}^{3} \lambda_i' \bar{\lambda}_i.$$

The two terms appearing on the left are conjugate to each other; thus the same is true of those on the right. This gives

$$\alpha \sum_{i=1}^{3} \lambda_i \bar{\lambda}_i' = \alpha' \sum_{i=1}^{3} \lambda_i \bar{\lambda}_i'.$$

Since $\alpha \neq \alpha'$, the factor of α or of α' is zero and orthogonality has been established.

We could proceed towards a proof of property 3 by means of similar though slightly more complicated calculations. However, at this point we invite the reader to show a certain amount of discouragement over the complexity of our calculations and to long for a development which frees us of too many subscripts, too many repeated summations, and other instruments of mental torture. Such a development is indeed forthcoming, and it is one of the contributions of high order made to mathematics via the spectral theorem mainstream. What is called for here is an intrinsic development of the theory of linear transformations, one that is independent of the base. Let us therefore assume that property 3 has been established.

We now have before us a complete logical analysis of the structure of the transformation H. Let us proceed to put the blocks together in an elegant, geometrically transparent manner. In the first place, it is apparent that our only reason for choosing euclidean three-space was in order to have notions of angle and orthogonality. Aside from that, symmetric transformations in three variables will be of practically no consequence. If we can introduce geometric concepts into n-dimensional spaces, everything we have said up to this moment will be valid in this more general setting. This is easy to do. First of all, by definition, n-space, $\mathfrak{E}_n$, consists of all vectors of the form $x = (\lambda_1, \cdots, \lambda_n)$ where the λ_i are complex numbers and where the operations of addition, $x + x'$, and of scalar multiplication, αx, are defined in the obvious way.† The notion of orthogonality of x to x' is then expressed by

$$\sum_{i=1}^{n} \lambda_i \bar{\lambda}_i' = 0.$$

Let us agree that the symmetric transformation H operates in euclidean n-space, $\mathfrak{E}_n$. Let α be one of its eigenvalues. If x and x' are eigenvectors corresponding to the value α, that is,

$$Hx = \alpha x, \, Hx' = \alpha x',$$

then obviously $x + x'$ and βx are also eigenvectors corresponding to the value α. This means that the totality of eigenvectors corresponding to a given eigenvalue constitute a *subspace* of $\mathfrak{E}_n$ (also called a *linear manifold*). For example, in the case of the transformation H defined earlier in three-space by $He_1 = e_1$, $He_2 = e_2$, $He_3 = 0$, the vectors in the "e_1, e_2 plane," that is, those of the form $\lambda e_1 + \mu e_2$, form a subspace (of two complex dimensions) corresponding to the eigenvalue 1, whereas the (one-dimensional) subspace of vectors of the form νe_3 corresponds to the eigenvalue 0. We notice that the two subspaces are orthogonal—that is, every vector of one is orthogonal to every vector of the other.

---

† It is assumed that n is an integer greater than zero. Note that if $n = 0$, then $\mathfrak{E}_0$ has one vector only: 0, and the zero and identity transformations are equal: $0 = I$. Our assumption brushes aside this possibility.

If $\mathfrak{M}$ is any linear subspace, let us write $\mathfrak{M}^\perp$ for the set of all vectors orthogonal to each vector in $\mathfrak{M}$. Then $\mathfrak{M}^\perp$ is clearly a linear manifold (for if y and y' are orthogonal to x, so are αy and $y + y'$). Note that $\mathfrak{M}$ and $\mathfrak{M}^\perp$ have only one element in common, $x = 0$. For if $x = (\lambda_1, \cdots, \lambda_n)$ is orthogonal to itself, then

$$\sum_{i=1}^{n} \lambda_i \bar{\lambda}_i = 0,$$

that is,

$$\sum_{i=1}^{n} |\lambda_i|^2 = 0,$$

hence $\lambda_i = 0$ for each i. Furthermore, every element x in $\mathfrak{E}_n$ can be "decomposed" in a unique way into two vectors y and z such that $y \in \mathfrak{M}$, $z \in \mathfrak{M}^\perp$, and $x = y + z$. We shall not give a proof of this fact since it requires a modest amount of discussion of the theory of linear manifolds.† The proof of the uniqueness of the decomposition follows immediately from the fact that $\mathfrak{M}$ and $\mathfrak{M}^\perp$ have only the vector 0 in common.

The characteristic property of symmetric transformations and the one that leads to the proof of property 3 is the following fact:

4. *Let α be an eigenvalue of H and let $\mathfrak{M}_\alpha$ be the linear manifold consisting of all eigenvectors corresponding to α. Let $\mathfrak{M}_\alpha^\perp$ be the manifold consisting of all vectors orthogonal to $\mathfrak{M}_\alpha$. Then if x is in $\mathfrak{M}_\alpha^\perp$, so also is Hx. Thus the analysis of the structure of H is completely determined by its structure on the two subspaces $\mathfrak{M}_\alpha$ and $\mathfrak{M}_\alpha^\perp$.*

Let us establish property 4. Let $x = (\lambda_1, \cdots, \lambda_n)$ and $y = (\mu_1, \cdots, \mu_n)$ be any two vectors. We shall introduce a new symbol which makes our calculations and our visualization of what is taking place much simpler. We define the *inner product* of x and y by:

(8) $$(x, y) = \lambda_1 \bar{\mu}_1 + \cdots + \lambda_n \bar{\mu}_n,$$

---

† For such a discussion, the reader is referred to the initial chapters of a treatise on vector spaces—for example, Halmos' book (footnote p. 132).

that is,

$$(x, y) = \sum_{i=1}^{n} \lambda_i \bar{\mu}_i.$$

In particular, if x is a vector in $\mathfrak{M}_\alpha$ (hence $Hx = \alpha x$) and y is a vector in $\mathfrak{M}_\alpha^\perp$, we have $(x, y) = 0$. Let us calculate (x, Hy). We have by the symmetry of H, for any vectors x and y (no matter how chosen),†

$$(9) \qquad\qquad (Hx, y) = (x, Hy),$$

as may be seen by a short calculation. Hence, in our special case we have

$$(x, Hy) = (Hx, y) = (\alpha x, y) = \alpha(x, y) = 0.$$

This states that Hy is in $\mathfrak{M}_\alpha^\perp$, which was to be proved.

The meaning of property 4 is this: According to the discussion following Eq. (7), there exists an eigenvalue α. We now consider the manifold $\mathfrak{M}_\alpha$ consisting of all eigenvectors corresponding to the eigenvalue α. We have not yet given nor do we propose to give a discussion of *dimensionality* of the subspaces of $\mathfrak{E}_n$. However, let us admit to our discussion the following facts: If the dimensions of $\mathfrak{M}_\alpha$ and $\mathfrak{M}_\alpha^\perp$ are r and s, then $s < n$ (since $r > 0$), and in fact, $r + s = n$. In $\mathfrak{M}_\alpha$ the structure of H is completely known: $H = \alpha I$ where I is the identity transformation. By our preceding discussion, if x is an arbitrary vector in $\mathfrak{E}_n$, $x = y + z$ where $y \in \mathfrak{M}_\alpha$ and $z \in \mathfrak{M}_\alpha^\perp$. We know the value of Hy; it remains to determine that of Hz.

By property 4, H transforms $\mathfrak{M}_\alpha$ into itself. Thus the problem of studying H on an n-dimensional space is now reduced to that of studying it on an s-dimensional space with $s < n$. If $s = 0$, we are finished—we know exactly how H is constructed. If not, we find an eigenvalue β of H on the s-dimensional space $\mathfrak{M}_\alpha^\perp$ and its associated manifold $\mathfrak{M}_\beta$ of eigenvectors. We continue in this

---

† Notice what beautiful simplicity is conveyed by this equation as compared to the subscript-studded

$$\eta_{ij} = \bar{\eta}_{ji}.$$

manner, obtaining a sequence of distinct eigenvalues $\alpha, \beta, \cdots$, and their associated manifolds of eigenvectors $\mathfrak{M}_\alpha, \mathfrak{M}_\beta, \cdots$. The vectors of the latter manifolds, of course, are orthogonal, each to each. Since the dimensionality n is finite, our process terminates after a finite number of steps.

We are now in a position to state the spectral theorem in euclidean n-space. Note that in the process of our discussion, we have virtually proved each of our assertions.

THE SPECTRAL THEOREM (simple form): *Let $\mathfrak{E}_n$ be complex n-dimensional space and let H be a symmetric linear transformation of $\mathfrak{E}_n$ into itself. Then there exists a finite number of distinct real numbers $\lambda_1, \cdots, \lambda_t$ and of closed linear manifolds $\mathfrak{M}_{\lambda_1}, \cdots, \mathfrak{M}_{\lambda_t}$ having nonzero dimensionality with the properties:*

1. *In $\mathfrak{M}_{\lambda_i}$, $H = \lambda_i I$. That is, the vectors of $\mathfrak{M}_{\lambda_i}$ are eigenvectors corresponding to the eigenvalue λ_i.*

2. *If $i \neq j$, $\mathfrak{M}_{\lambda_i} \perp \mathfrak{M}_{\lambda_j}$, meaning that every vector in one manifold is orthogonal to every vector in the other.*

3. *The manifolds $\mathfrak{M}_{\lambda_i}$ span $\mathfrak{E}_n$ in the following sense: If x is a vector in $\mathfrak{E}_n$, then there exist unique vectors x_i in $\mathfrak{M}_{\lambda_i}$ such that*

$$x = x_1 + \cdots + x_t.$$

The numbers λ_i and the manifolds $\mathfrak{M}_{\lambda_i}$ are uniquely determined by H.

Let us inquire into an interpretation of this result. In the space $\mathfrak{E}_n$ we have as basis the vectors

$$e_1 = (1, 0, \cdots, 0), \cdots, e_n = (0, \cdots 0, 1).$$

Let us choose n distinct real numbers $\lambda_1, \cdots, \lambda_n$ and construct the matrix (η_{ij}) whose elements are all zero with the exception of those in the "main diagonal" where we distribute the λ_i "from northwest to southeast." Then (η_{ij}) is symmetric and the associated transformation H has the λ_i as eigenvalues and has as associated manifolds $\mathfrak{M}_{\lambda_i}$ the one-dimensional spaces generated by e_i. If we had chosen the λ_i not necessarily distinct, then the associated manifolds would have "coalesced" into fewer manifolds of higher dimensionality. This is one aspect of the situation described in the main theorem.

There is an important difference between the above example and the result of the spectral theorem. In general, the manifolds $\mathfrak{M}_{\lambda_i}$ are not generated by the "principal axes" e_i. However, it is always possible to choose a new orthogonal basis $b_1, \cdots, b_n$ in $\mathfrak{E}_n$ such that each manifold $\mathfrak{M}_{\lambda_i}$ is spanned by a certain collection of the b_j. In other words, the original axes e_i are not proper for the study of H; but for every H, there is a proper set of orthogonal axes with respect to which H is a magnification in the direction of each axis.

Before we leave this discussion of the phenomena in n-dimensional space and turn to the subject proper of this paper, we shall state and prove the converse to the spectral theorem. In a sense, the spectral theorem states that every symmetric transformation in $\mathfrak{E}_n$ can be constructed from elementary transformations each of which is of the form $H = \lambda I$ where λ is real. The converse theorem states that *every transformation H constructed by setting $H = \lambda_i I$ on pairwise orthogonal manifolds $\mathfrak{M}_{\lambda_i}$ is symmetric.*

We shall replace the definition of the symmetry of H with the equivalent given in Eq. (9): $(Hx, y) = (x, Hy)$ is valid for every pair of vectors x, y. Note that if Eq. (9) holds, then

$$\eta_{ij} = (He_j, e_i) = (e_j, He_i) = (\overline{He_i, e_j}) = \bar{\eta}_{ji},$$

where we have used Eq. (8). Conversely, if $\eta_{ij} = \bar{\eta}_{ji}$, then

$$(He_j, e_i) = (e_j, He_i)$$

and since every vector x, or y can be expressed as a linear combination of the e_i, we find that by a simple and not uninteresting calculation, $(Hx, y) = (x, Hy)$.

In proving the converse of the spectral theorem, we shall assume for the sake of simplicity that we have only two distinct eigenvalues, λ_1 and λ_2, and that the associated manifolds $\mathfrak{M}_{\lambda_1}$ and $\mathfrak{M}_{\lambda_2}$ span $\mathfrak{E}_n$; that is, given x in $\mathfrak{E}_n$, there exist x_1 in $\mathfrak{M}_{\lambda_1}$ and x_2 in $\mathfrak{M}_{\lambda_2}$ such that $x = x_1 + x_2$. If, for an arbitrary y, we set similarly

$y = y_1 + y_2$, we have for i and $j = 1$ or 2:

$$(Hx_i, y_j) = (\lambda_i x_i, y_j) = \lambda_i \delta_{ij}(x_i, y_j)$$

$$= \lambda_j \delta_{ij}(x_i, y_j) = (x_i, \lambda_j y_j) = (x_i, Hy_j),$$

where $\delta_{ij} = 1$ if $i = j$, and $\delta_{ij} = 0$ otherwise. By the linearity of H, this establishes Eq. (9). The converse of the spectral theorem is therefore established.

This concludes the preliminary discussion on the basis of which the general spectral theorem will be analyzed. We shall proceed to a description of the setting against which the main theorem can be silhouetted. Here and there, there will appear some remarks of historical content. We make no pretense of giving even a barely adequate historical account. The usual and rapid enumeration of a few names qualified by a short phrase can hardly begin to cover the long history of this brilliant theorem. The purpose of the bibliography we cite is to give reference to a few original papers and to indicate one or two books in which the matter may be pursued. The best book to recommend is a complete one whose material is accessible and which the reader refuses to close.

2. HILBERT SPACE

The development we have traced of the spectral theorem in n-dimensional complex euclidean space, $\mathfrak{E}_n$, has been known for approximately one century. Although the finite-dimensional case is enormously useful in myriads of applications, the true development of the ideas we have introduced in the discussion of our preliminary example does not take place on a panoramic scale until we consider infinite-dimensional spaces. It is in the discussion of these spaces that we perceive an amalgamation in heroic proportions of portions of analysis, geometry, and applied mathematics: function spaces, differential and integral equations, operator theory, abstract Fourier series, geometry of manifolds, weak, strong, and uniform topologies, theory of spectra, quantum mechanics, and others.

A complex euclidean space of infinitely many dimensions is called a *Hilbert space*.† This name is derived from the fact that Hilbert discussed the first realization of the abstract concept. The type of space—call it $\mathfrak{H}$—which was introduced by Hilbert, is as follows: The vectors of $\mathfrak{H}$ are the sequences of complex numbers $x = (\lambda_1, \lambda_2, \cdot \cdot \cdot)$ with addition, $x + x'$, scalar multiplication, αx, defined in the "natural" (sometimes called the "obvious") way. This gives an algebraic structure to the space, but as yet we have no geometrical structure. For the latter, we must be able to speak of the length of a vector and of the angle between two vectors. The length is introduced as in *n-space* by the formula

$$\|x\| = \sqrt{|\lambda_1|^2 + |\lambda_2|^2 + \cdot \cdot \cdot} = (\sum_{i=1}^{\infty} |\lambda_i|^2)^{1/2}.$$

This implies that we must restrict ourselves to vectors $x = (\lambda_1, \lambda_2, \cdot \cdot \cdot)$ for which

$$\sum_{i=1}^{\infty} |\lambda_i|^2 < \infty.$$

With only this restriction, the entire development proceeds and the door is open to the new phenomena we have mentioned.

We shall not proceed along this road. It may be noticed that the space $\mathfrak{H}$ resembles the space $\mathfrak{C}_n$ in that the vectors of both spaces are described with reference to a specific basis. In $\mathfrak{H}$, the basis is

$$e_1 = (1, 0, 0, \cdot \cdot \cdot), \qquad e_2 = (0, 1, 0, \cdot \cdot \cdot),$$

and so on. This is an unfortunate circumstance, if it cannot be avoided. For example, we have seen that in the case of symmetric transformations, the problem of the determination of structure is complicated by the fact that a "choice of coordinates" is given at the outset. The ultimate answers express no preference for the initial coordinates. Indeed, for each problem there seems to be an ideal set of coordinates, and these vary from problem to problem.

---

† Accurate enough for our purposes. However, it should be stated that: (1) there are real as well as complex Hilbert spaces; (2) some authors use the term also for finite-dimensional spaces.

This suggests that we look upon our spaces in a manner that is unprejudiced by a choice of coordinates. A development that adopts this point of view is said to be *intrinsic*. Intrinsic methods in Hilbert space were introduced by John von Neumann in 1929. As will be apparent shortly, the concepts are very simple and the saving in energy that would otherwise be devoted to questions of indices, summations, convergence, is enormous.

By definition, $\mathfrak{H}$ is a mathematical object (structure) which has the various attributes described briefly below. The objects in $\mathfrak{H}$ are *vectors* denoted by $x, y, z, x', \cdots$. For these vectors we define two algebraic operations: vector addition, $x + x'$, and scalar multiplication, αx, where α is any complex number.† These operations are subject to "natural" or "obvious" laws, sometimes also called the "usual" laws of (vector) algebra. We shall not exhibit them all here, but they will be apparent by analogy to the finite-dimensional case previously discussed. For example, we shall have:

$$\alpha(x + x') = \alpha x + \alpha x', \qquad (\alpha + \beta)x = \alpha x + \beta x, \quad 1x = x,$$

and so on.

The geometric structure is introduced into $\mathfrak{H}$ by defining for every pair of vectors x and y an "inner product," written (x, y). This inner product is a complex number. It is the inner product that will determine the "angle" between x and x' and also will determine the "length" of the vector x. Let us meet an objection at this point. The reader may say: "I do not conceive of this angle and I cannot grasp the concept of length because of the number of dimensions." In fact, the answers to this objection are not long and they are convincing. Let us, however, settle the matter this way: We shall henceforth, starting with the next paragraph, never refer to either "angle" or "length"! To return to the inner product (x, y), it too will be endowed with a variety of properties which may be surmised by the situation in $\mathfrak{E}_n$. We suggest that the reader return to a consideration of Eq. (8), which

---

† The axioms of a vector space are beginning to be a commonplace. They may be found in the books mentioned on page 132.

will make meaningful the following properties of the inner product:

(10a) $$(x + x', y) = (x, y) + (x', y);$$

(10b) $$(\alpha x, y) = \alpha(x, y);$$

(10c) $$(y, x) = \overline{(x, y)};$$

(10d) $(x, x) \geq 0$ and $(x, x) = 0$ if and only if $x = 0$.

Let us make some remarks. Using Eq. (10c), we see that (x, x) is real; Eq. (10d) asserts that the real number is not negative. The "0" in "$x = 0$" is the vector "0" having the property

$$x + 0 = 0 + x = x$$

for every x. It should not be mistaken for the number "0" which is written the same way. The next calculation uses both the number "0" and the vector "0": Let $x \neq 0$; then $0 \cdot x = 0$. Hence

$$(0, 0) = (0x, 0) = 0(x, 0) = 0,$$

using Eq. (10b). This explains Eq. (10d), in part.

The number $\sqrt{(x, x)}$ will be denoted by $\|x\|$ and will be called the *norm* of x.† This norm has the following properties:

(11a) $\|x\| \geq 0;$ $\|x\| = 0$ if and only if $x = 0;$

(11b) $$\|\alpha x\| = |\alpha| \, \|x\|;$$

(11c) $$\|x + y\| \leq \|x\| + \|y\|.$$

The only property that is not immediate is (11c). This results immediately from

$$\|x + y\|^2 = (x + y, x + y)$$
$$= (x, x) + (y, x) + (x, y) + (y, y)$$
$$= \|x\|^2 + 2 \text{ real } (x, y) + \|y\|^2$$

---

† In the previous paragraph, we would have said "length" instead of "norm."

and from the *Cauchy inequality*,

$$(12) \qquad |(xy)| \leq \|x\| \cdot \|y\|,$$

which is not difficult to prove.

The properties grouped in (11) assert that $\mathfrak{H}$ is a metric space providing that the distance between x and y is defined to be $\|x - y\|$. We shall require that the space $\mathfrak{H}$ be *complete* in this metric. This requirement states that if $\{x_n\}$ is a sequence of vectors in $\mathfrak{H}$ such that $\|x_n - x_m\| \longrightarrow 0$, then there exists a vector x in $\mathfrak{H}$ such that $\|x - x_n\| \longrightarrow 0$. The abstract completion of metric spaces is a very easy matter. Thus every metric space may be "immersed" in a complete metric space of which it is a dense subset. For example, the completion of the rational numbers gives the real numbers. A space that has an inner product but that is not complete is sometimes called "a space with an inner product."

A final requirement for our abstract space $\mathfrak{H}$, which we insist on only because interesting and new applications lie in this direction, is that it should be *infinite-dimensional*. This concept may be defined as follows: For each positive integer n, there exist n vectors, $x_1, \cdots, x_n$, such that an equation of the form

$$(13) \qquad \alpha_1 x_1 + \cdots + \alpha_n x_n = 0$$

is satisfied only if $\alpha_1 = 0, \cdots, \alpha_n = 0$. In other words, for every n there exist n linearly independent vectors.

It is not difficult to show that each Hilbert space has a dimensionality which is one of the infinite cardinal numbers. In addition, any two Hilbert spaces of the same dimension are "essentially" identical (algebraically and metrically isomorphic).

Let us consider some examples of such spaces. The first example is that due to Hilbert and which we have already examined. That space is sometimes denoted by l^2. Consider now the set of all continuous complex-valued functions, $x = x(t)$, $0 \leq t \leq 1$. If addition and scalar multiplication are defined in the usual manner, these form a vector space. We may introduce an inner product into this space by the definition

$$(14) \qquad (x, y) = \int_0^1 x(t)\overline{y(t)} \, dt,$$

where the integral is that of Riemann. This inner product has, indeed, all the properties listed in (10). The space clearly has infinite dimensionality. However, in the metric of the norm, the space is not complete.† The space may be made complete, but although the abstract statement of that fact is essentially a rather shallow assertion, the specific realization of completeness requires the development of an entirely new theory of integration: the integral of Lebesgue. Granted the existence of the latter, we may say: The Lebesgue measurable functions, $x = x(t)$, which are square integrable, constitute a complex Hilbert space with inner product given by Eq. (14), providing that two functions be considered identical whenever they differ at a set of points of Lebesgue measure zero. This space is represented by the symbol L^2. The proof of the completeness of this space is the content of the theorem announced simultaneously by Riesz and Fischer in 1907.‡ The theorem may be given the following interpretation: Every measurable function $x = x(t)$ which is square integrable has Fourier coefficients§ $\lambda_1, \lambda_2, \cdots$ for which

$$(15) \qquad \sum_{i=1}^{\infty} |\lambda_i|^2 = \int_0^1 |x(t)|^2 \, dt.$$

Conversely, for every convergent series $\sum_{i=1}^{\infty} |\lambda_i|^2$, there exists a

---

† It is not difficult to construct a sequence of continuous functions $\{f_n\}$ having the properties: (1) $\{f_n\}$ is monotone increasing; (2) $f_n(t) \longrightarrow 1$ for $0 \leq t < \frac{1}{2}$; $f_n(t) = 0$ for $\frac{1}{2} \leq t \leq 1$; (3) $\|f_n - f_m\| \longrightarrow 0$; (4) there is no continuous function f such that $\|f - f_n\| \longrightarrow 0$.

‡ The following story about a café was recounted to me in a café. Many years after 1907, some mathematicians who had been attending a continental congress at which men of many nationalities were present, retired after a formal scientific session to its analytic continuation: the amenities of a charming café. After some time, one of the scientists turned to Fred Riesz and said to him: "By the way, have you ever met Fischer? He has been sitting one foot away from you at the next table all this time." This was their first meeting.

§ The classic Fourier coefficients of $f(t)$ are obtained by integrating $f(t)$ $\cos 2n\pi t$ and $f(t) \sin 2n\pi t$. In the present case, we shall have to modify these coefficients by multiplying them by well-known constants.

square integrable function $x(t)$ whose Fourier coefficients are
$\lambda_1, \lambda_2, \cdots$. This theorem illustrates how Hilbert's original
space l^2 and the space L^2 of square integrable functions are
isomorphic. It suffices to map the function $x \in L^2$ into the
vector $(\lambda_1, \lambda_2, \cdots)$ consisting of its Fourier coefficients in l^2.

We state once more that the vector x is said to be orthogonal
to the vector y if and only if $(x, y) = 0$. It is clear from properties (10a) and (10b) that if x and x' are orthogonal to y, so are
$x + x'$ and αx.

3. LINEAR TRANSFORMATIONS

We shall be interested in the study of linear transformations
of the space $\mathfrak{H}$ into itself. Such a transformation H is defined by
the properties exhibited in (1) and (2). For the first time, we
meet the necessity of introducing topological considerations,
without which the study of the theory of linear transformations
in infinite-dimensional spaces is essentially meaningless. With
the help of these notions we can then consider transformations
which are continuous. In the finite-dimensional case, all linear
transformations are continuous in terms of any topology which
it is reasonable to use. Because of this fact, they can be studied
without even the mention of topology.

We have already introduced a topology in $\mathfrak{H}$ by means of our
metric, $\|x\|$. As we have pointed out, the vector x is "close" to
the vector "y" if the real number $\|x - y\|$ is "small." With the
help of this topology, we can define the continuity of the linear
transformation H: we say that H is *continuous* providing that
Hx is close to Hy when x is close to y. Suppose that there exists
a constant $k \geq 0$ such that for all x in $\mathfrak{H}$,

(16) $$\|Hx\| \leq k\|x\|.$$

Then clearly

$$\|Hx - Hy\| = \|H(x - y)\| \leq k\|x - y\|.$$

This proves that H is continuous. The converse proposition can
also be proved without difficulty. That is, if H is continuous,

there exists a number $k \geq 0$ such that (16) is satisfied. The number k is called a *bound* of H, and H is called a *bounded transformation*. It has been customary for the most part to speak of bounded linear transformations rather than continuous linear transformations and we shall adopt this usage here. Finally, let us add that the smallest number k satisfying (16) is called *the* bound of H and is denoted by $\|H\|$. Thus we have

(16') $$\|Hx\| \leq \|H\| \, \|x\|.$$

We are ready now to start to indicate the subject matter of the spectral theorem. The spectral theorem gives a complete analysis of transformations, H, in Hilbert space which are (a) linear, (b) symmetric, and (c) continuous. That is, H satisfies (1), (2), (9), and (16). However, let us state unequivocally at this point that the concept of the continuity of H introduced above is subject to important variations. It turns out that the general bounded transformation in (16) has a structure much more complicated than that which we could expect after our study of $\mathfrak{E}_n$. Furthermore, there is a natural class, the class of *completely continuous* transformations, which has a structure that can be easily understood in terms of our preliminary example. There is a second class of transformations H which are not bounded in the sense of (16') but which *turn out* to be the limit of sequences $\{H_n\}$ of transformations satisfying (16') in which the bound $\|H_n\|$ increases without limit. This type of symmetric transformation is called *unbounded*. In the pages which follow we shall describe the structure of transformations which fall under (a) the completely continuous case, (b) the continuous or bounded case, and (c) the unbounded case. Before doing so, we shall consider some very special symmetric transformations and their relation to the geometry of the Hilbert space—namely, the projections.

We note as before that the zero transformation O defined by $Ox = 0$ for all x and the identity transformation I defined by $Ix = x$ for all x are linear bounded symmetric transformations. The same is true of the scalar transformation αI defined by $(\alpha I)x = \alpha x$ in case α is real. Note that we have $\|\alpha I\| = |\alpha|$ by (11b).

In the discussion of $\mathfrak{E}_n$, we defined a linear manifold to be a subset of $\mathfrak{E}_n$ with the following property: If x and x' are in the subset, so are $x + x'$ and αx. This concept of linear manifold, which is completely algebraic, is insufficient for our purposes and must be modified by topological considerations. We shall be concerned with *closed* linear manifolds, that is, with linear manifolds which contain all their limit points, the limits being considered in the norm topology. (That is, if $\{x_n\}$ is a convergent sequence of vectors in the manifold and $x_n \longrightarrow x$, then x is also in the manifold.) In subsequent discussions, we shall frequently use the word "manifold" to indicate a closed linear manifold.

Let $\mathfrak{M}$ be a manifold. Let $\mathfrak{M}^\perp$ denote the set of all vectors y which are orthogonal to each vector x in $\mathfrak{M}$, thus for which $(x, y) = 0$. It is easy to show that $\mathfrak{M}^\perp$ is linear and closed, and hence is a manifold. It is called the *orthogonal complement* of $\mathfrak{M}$. It may be shown that $\mathfrak{M}$ is the orthogonal complement of $\mathfrak{M}^\perp$. Clearly, the only element common to both $\mathfrak{M}$ and $\mathfrak{M}^\perp$ is $x = 0$; furthermore, it may be shown that the two manifolds *span* $\mathfrak{H}$ in the sense that if x is an arbitrary vector in $\mathfrak{H}$, there exist two vectors y and z such that

$$(17) \qquad x = y + z, \qquad y \text{ in } \mathfrak{M}, \quad z \text{ in } \mathfrak{M}^\perp.$$

This decomposition is unique. Also, it is clear that if x' has the decomposition $x' = y' + z'$, then $x + x'$ has the decomposition

$$x + x' = (y + y') + (z + z'),$$

and αx has the decomposition $\alpha x = \alpha y + \alpha z$. Define a transformation P by means of the equation

$$(18) \qquad Px = y.$$

That P is a linear transformation is the substance of our immediately preceding remarks. Next, note that since

$$
\begin{aligned}
(19) \qquad \|x\|^2 = (x, x) &= (y + z, y + z) \\
&= (y, y) + (z, y) + (y, z) + (z, z) \\
&= \|y\|^2 + \|z\|^2,
\end{aligned}
$$

wherein we have used the fact that y is orthogonal to z, we have

$$\|y\| = \|Px\| \leq \|x\|.$$

Thus P is bounded† and $\|P\| \leq 1$. Finally, P is symmetric as may be seen from the calculation (using the notations given a few lines earlier)

$$(Px, x') = (y, y' + z') = (y, y') + (y, z')$$
$$= (y, y') = (y + z, y')$$
$$= (x, Px').$$

An additional fact is that for any vector x, we have

$$P(Px) = Py = y = Px.$$

We write this in the form $P^2 = P$; we say that P is an *idempotent transformation*.

Thus, to any pair $\mathfrak{M}$ and $\mathfrak{N}$ of manifolds, each of which is the orthogonal complement of the other, we may associate a *projection* P on one of the manifolds. This projection is a bounded linear and symmetric transformation which satisfies $P^2 = P$. The converse proposition, which will not be proved here but will be left as an interesting exercise to the reader, is this: Given a bounded linear and symmetric transformation P which satisfies $P^2 = P$, then there is associated with it a pair of manifolds $\mathfrak{M}$ and $\mathfrak{N}$, each of which is the orthogonal complement of the other. Indeed, $\mathfrak{M}$ is the manifold of elements x such that $Px = x$; and $\mathfrak{N}$ is the manifold of elements x such that $Px = 0$. Note that the only eigenvalues of P are 1 and 0 and that $\mathfrak{M}$ and $\mathfrak{N}$ are the associated manifolds of eigenvectors.

The projections are the building brick by means of which the general symmetric transformation is obtained. This is obviously a vague statement, but it is a most suggestive one, and we shall suggest at this point the manner in which these "bricks" are put together. First, let us discuss some important preliminary considerations.

---

† In fact $\|P\| = 1$ always unless $P = O$, in which case $\|P\| = 0$.

If H and H' are transformations, there is defined the transformation $H + H'$ by means of the equation:

$$(H + H')x = Hx + H'x$$

for each x in $\mathfrak{H}$. It is trivial to check that if H and H' are linear, so is $H + H'$; if H and H' are symmetric, so is their sum. Finally, if H and H' are bounded, the calculation

$$\|(H + H')x\| = \|Hx + H'x\| \leq \|Hx\| + \|H'x\|$$
$$\leq (\|H\| + \|H'\|)\,\|x\|,$$

in which we have used (11c) and (16′), shows that $H + H'$ is bounded and that

(20) $\|H + H'\| \leq \|H\| + \|H'\|.$

The transformation αH is defined by $(\alpha H)x = \alpha(Hx)$. It may be seen immediately that αH is linear and bounded when H is and is symmetric if α is real. Furthermore, we have

(21) $\|\alpha H\| = |\alpha| \cdot \|H\|.$

We have shown that the set of all bounded linear transformations constitutes a vector space. In this vector space, a norm may be introduced by associating the real number $\|H\|$ to any transformation H. The norm satisfies (20), (21), and

(22) $\|H\| \geq 0;$ $\|H\| = 0$ if and only if $H = O.$

Such a vector space is called a *normed vector space*. The norm gives a metric in the space in which the distance between H and H' is taken to be $\|H - H'\|$. It may be established that the space is complete in this norm in the sense defined in Section 2.

Let us return to the discussion of projections. It is clear that if P and P' are projections, then $P + P'$ and αP are symmetric transformations if α is real. Our first glimpse of the significance of the general spectral theorem is contained in the following statement: *A bounded linear transformation H is symmetric if and only if it can be approximated in the norm by sums of the type*

$$\sum_{i=1}^{n} \alpha_i P_i$$

where the P_i are projections and the α_i are real. In other words, the projections and their finite real linear combinations lie dense in the real vector space of the symmetric transformations. Now although this statement is correct, it reveals only the outer shell of the spectral theorem, for the essential feature of the theorem concerns the type of projections P_i which are allowed to enter into the approximation. The description of these will be put off until later and will be based on geometric considerations. However, one algebraic feature of importance in the approximation may be mentioned in advance: All the transformations which are involved in it are *commutative*. We remind the reader that two transformations H and H' are commutative if and only if $H(H'x) = H'(Hx)$ for every x; thus, commutativity is expressed by the equation

$$(23) \qquad\qquad\qquad HH' = H'H.$$

4. COMPLETELY CONTINUOUS TRANSFORMATIONS

We are now in a position to obtain a good geometric picture of the structure of symmetric transformations H which are not merely continuous, but *completely continuous*, which we define below:

A bounded linear transformation H is said to be completely continuous if it has the following property: If $\{x_n\}$ is any bounded sequence of vectors in $\mathfrak{H}$—and boundedness means that $\|x_n\| \le k$ for some k and all n—the sequence $\{Hx_n\}$ contains a (at least one) convergent subsequence.

The condition of complete continuity on H is a very strong one. It implies that H is very similar in its behavior to a transformation acting in a finite-dimensional space. The similarity can be stated in the form that H can be approximated by transformations of "finite character." We shall see that for symmetric transformations H, the spectral theorem reflects this finite character and gives a structure which is the most naive possible generalization of the one in $\mathfrak{E}_n$.

The notion of complete continuity came to the fore through the study of integral equations. An example of an integral equation is the following:

$$(24) \qquad g(x) = \lambda f(x) - \int_a^b K(x, y)f(y)\, dy$$

where g, K, and λ are given in advance and f is the unknown. The linear operator K defined by

$$Kf = h, \qquad h(x) = \int_a^b K(x, y)f(y)\, dy,$$

is completely continuous. Equation (24) was first solved by Fredholm in 1900.† The topological properties of the operator K were noticed somewhat later. It is an interesting circumstance that although mathematicians have long been concerned with differential equations—whose theory can be considerably more than mildly complicated—integral equations attracted attention rather late, despite the fact that they are much easier to handle. It was through integral equations that mathematicians became interested in vector spaces of infinite dimensions, in Hilbert space, and later in general Banach spaces. Thus, in a very real sense, the key to this paradise was the completely continuous transformation.

Note that not all continuous transformations are completely continuous. For example, since we insisted in Section 2 that the space $\mathfrak{H}$ be infinite-dimensional, the identity transformation, I, is not completely continuous. In particular, if we consider the original Hilbert space, l^2, with its associated basis, $e_1, e_2, e_3, \cdots$, we see that $\{e_n\}$ is a bounded sequence since $\|e_n\| = 1$ for each n, but $\{Ie_n\} = \{e_n\}$ contains no convergent subsequence. In fact, $\|e_n - e_m\| = \sqrt{2}$ if $n \neq m$. Note also that in the n-dimensional space $\mathfrak{E}_n$, every continuous linear transformation is completely continuous.

We shall dissect briefly a completely continuous and symmetric transformation H. We have developed the intuitive ideas and the vocabulary necessary for this task in the preceding sections.

---

† We refer the reader to the book by F. Riesz and B. Sz.-Nagy, *Leçons d'analyse fonctionelle*, Académie des Sciences de Hongrie, 1953. Its bibliography contains the exact data for the works mentioned in this paper.

Thus it will be possible to give an understandable account of the results. However, with a few exceptions, it will no longer be possible to give proofs nor refer them to standard mathematical background.

Relying upon our previous experience, we see that the first problem to face is the eigenvalue problem: *Find all numbers* λ *such that there exists a vector* $x \neq 0$ *such that* $Hx = \lambda x$. Suppose for one moment that the eigenvalue problem can be solved in the sense that we can prove that there exists at least one eigenvalue and one corresponding eigenvector. Given this initial knowledge, the structure problem for H can be rapidly unraveled. As before, it is easy to establish properties 1 and 2 given in Section 1; that is, all eigenvalues are real, and eigenvectors belonging to distinct eigenvalues are orthogonal. Property 4 may also be established immediately. Next we have that

5. *If* $\lambda \neq 0$ *is an eigenvalue and* $\mathfrak{M}_\lambda$ *is the closed linear manifold of associated eigenvectors, then* $\mathfrak{M}_\lambda$ *is finite-dimensional.*

This is so because, in $\mathfrak{M}_\lambda$, H is the transformation λI, and since H is completely continuous and $\lambda \neq 0$, $\mathfrak{M}_\lambda$ is necessarily finite-dimensional.

It is clear that if the eigenvalue problem can be solved in the sense explained in the previous paragraph, the structure problem for H is essentially solved also. Let us look briefly at the eigenvalue problem. In the space $\mathfrak{E}_n$, this problem gave rise to a problem in determinants and linear equations in n unknowns. The problem in $\mathfrak{H}$ cannot be expressed in these terms. The theory of infinite-dimensional determinants does not exist. However, alternative methods for the solution of the eigenvalue problem were obtained. In particular, methods were developed proving the existence of an "extreme" eigenvalue λ, for which $|\lambda| = \|H\|$.

The case in which $\lambda = 0$ is an eigenvalue causes a bit of trouble and is best handled separately as follows:

Let $\mathfrak{M}_0$ be the manifold of eigenvectors corresponding to the eigenvalue $\lambda = 0$. Thus $\mathfrak{M}_0$ consists of the vector 0 if H does not have $\lambda = 0$ as eigenvalue. Then, as we have seen, H transforms $\mathfrak{M}_0^\perp$ into itself and is completely continuous and symmetric on $\mathfrak{M}_0^\perp$. If $\mathfrak{M}_0^\perp$ is finite-dimensional, we apply the spectral theorem in $\mathfrak{E}_n$. If $\mathfrak{M}_0^\perp$ is infinite-dimensional, it is itself a Hilbert space. Note that in $\mathfrak{M}_0^\perp$, H does not have $\lambda = 0$ as an eigenvalue.

We shall assume henceforth that H does not have $\lambda = 0$ as eigenvalue and hence that $\mathfrak{M}_0^\perp = \mathfrak{H}$.

Let $\alpha > 0$ be a real constant. We shall see that there exist only a finite number of eigenvalues λ with $|\lambda| > \alpha$. The argument runs along these lines: Suppose we had an infinite set of distinct eigenvalues λ_n with $|\lambda_n| > \alpha$ and suppose that ϕ_n are associated characteristic vectors chosen so that $\|\phi_n\| = 1$. Then the ϕ_n are orthogonal. Let us apply the definition of complete continuity to the bounded sequence $\{\phi_n\}$. We have $\{H\phi_n\} = \{\lambda_n\phi_n\}$; furthermore, an easy calculation shows that for $n \neq m$,

$$\|\lambda_n\phi_n - \lambda_m\phi_m\|^2 = \lambda_n^2 + \lambda_m^2 > 2\alpha^2.$$

Thus no subsequence of $\{H\phi_n\}$ is convergent. All this implies that the eigenvalues can be arranged in a sequence $\lambda_1, \lambda_2, \lambda_3, \cdots$ with $|\lambda_1| \geq |\lambda_2| \geq \cdots$. The sequence is indeed infinite since a finite number of manifolds "absorb" from $\mathfrak{H}$ only finite dimensionality (see below). Thus we have $\lambda_n \longrightarrow 0$.

Let $\mathfrak{M}_1, \mathfrak{M}_2, \cdots$ be the sequence of manifolds of eigenvectors corresponding to the eigenvalues $\lambda_1, \lambda_2, \cdots$. We have seen that $\mathfrak{M}_n \perp \mathfrak{M}_m$ (meaning $\mathfrak{M}_n$ is orthogonal to $\mathfrak{M}_m$) if $n \neq m$. For any two orthogonal manifolds $\mathfrak{M}_n$ and $\mathfrak{M}_m$, we write $\mathfrak{M}_n \oplus \mathfrak{M}_m$ to indicate the manifold (obviously linear, and also closed) of elements $x_n + x_m$, where x_n is in $\mathfrak{M}_n$ and x_m is in $\mathfrak{M}_m$. In a similar way, we may write a finite sum

$$(25) \qquad\qquad \mathfrak{M}_1 \oplus \cdots \oplus \mathfrak{M}_n$$

to represent the closed linear manifold of vectors of the form $x_1 + \cdots + x_n$, where x_i is in $\mathfrak{M}_i$, $i = 1, \cdots, n$. Since the eigenvalues form an infinite sequence $\lambda_1, \lambda_2, \cdots$, then a rather obvious meaning can be given to the infinite sum,

$$(26) \qquad\qquad \mathfrak{M}_1 \oplus \mathfrak{M}_2 \oplus \cdots,$$

namely, the infinite sum is to be the smallest closed linear manifold which contains each $\mathfrak{M}_n$. In this case, it may be shown that this infinite sum is the entire space $\mathfrak{H}$.† This means that every element x in $\mathfrak{H}$ may be approximated in the norm by elements belonging to finite sums. We may write this in the form

$$(27) \qquad x = x_1 + x_2 + \cdots .$$

This equation implies that $\|x\|^2 = \|x_1\|^2 + \|x_2\|^2 + \cdots .$ We have also that

$$(28) \qquad Hx = \lambda_1 x_1 + \lambda_2 x_2 + \cdots ,$$

with $\|Hx\|^2 = \lambda_1^2 \|x_1\|^2 + \lambda_2^2 \|x_2\|^2 + \cdots .$ We are now in a position to sum up.

THE SPECTRAL THEOREM (completely continuous case): *Let H be a completely continuous transformation in Hilbert space $\mathfrak{H}$ and such that $Hx = 0$ has no solutions $x \neq 0$. Then there exists a sequence of distinct real numbers λ_1, λ_2, $\cdots$ and an associated sequence of closed linear manifolds $\mathfrak{M}_1$, $\mathfrak{M}_2$, $\cdots$, each having nonzero dimensionality with the properties:*

1. *In $\mathfrak{M}_i$, $H = \lambda_i I$. That is, the vectors of $\mathfrak{M}_i$ are eigenvectors of H corresponding to the eigenvalue λ_i.*
2. *If $i \neq j$, then $\mathfrak{M}_i \perp \mathfrak{M}_j$.*
3. *The manifolds $\mathfrak{M}_n$ span $\mathfrak{H}$ in the sense that the sum in (26) is $\mathfrak{H}$; or equivalently, that an expansion (27) is valid for every x in $\mathfrak{H}$.*
4. *The manifolds $\mathfrak{M}_n$ each have finite dimensionality.*
5. *The sequence $\{\lambda_n\}$ converges to zero.*

The numbers λ_i and the manifolds $\mathfrak{M}_i$ are uniquely determined by H.

---

† To prove this fact, let the manifold represented by the sum in (26) be denoted by $\mathfrak{M}$. Consider $\mathfrak{M}^\perp$. If $\mathfrak{M}^\perp \neq 0$, then knowing that H is completely continuous and symmetric in $\mathfrak{M}^\perp$, we obtain an eigenvalue λ of H in $\mathfrak{M}^\perp$ and proceed as before. Since this contradicts our agreement that λ_1, λ_2, $\cdots$ represents *all* eigenvalues of H, we have $\mathfrak{M}^\perp = 0$, hence $\mathfrak{M} = \mathfrak{H}$.

This, then, is the spectral theorem in this case. We note that it represents essentially the minimum of new features which one could reasonably expect over the spectral theorem in $\mathfrak{E}_n$. Note also that this is the theorem which applies to classical integral equations. Finally, the converse proposition is easily stated and may easily be proved to be valid. That is, given two sequences $\{\lambda_n\}$ and $\{\mathfrak{M}_n\}$ which satisfy the various conditions given above, we may "put together" a transformation H which is symmetric and completely continuous for which the two sequences give the complete solution of the eigenvalue and eigenvector problem.

We turn now to a much more difficult case, the case in which H is continuous but not necessarily completely continuous. We have seen earlier that continuity is equivalent to boundedness as defined in (16) and (16′). For that reason, we refer to this case as the "bounded case."

5. BOUNDED TRANSFORMATIONS

Our problem now is to consider the structure of a general bounded transformation in Hilbert space. The jump in complexity from the previous case to the present one is staggering. Here we meet for the first time the phenomenon of the *continuous spectrum*. In order to understand this concept, we shall have to return to our discussion of the eigenvalue problem which up to the present has been rather elementary and which needs to be made considerably more sophisticated.

Let H be any bounded linear transformation and λ a complex number. Consider the transformation $H_\lambda = H - \lambda I$, which is also linear and bounded. There may exist a vector $x \neq 0$ such that $(H - \lambda I)x = 0$, that is, such that $H_\lambda x = 0$. This is precisely the case which has received attention up to the present and which has been discussed as the "eigenvalue problem." If such an x exists, we shall say that λ belongs to the *point spectrum* of H.

Suppose that no such x exists. Then the only solution of $H_\lambda x = 0$ is $x = 0$. This implies that H_λ maps the space $\mathfrak{H}$ into itself in a one-to-one way. We shall let $\mathfrak{R}_\lambda$ denote the *range* of H_λ, that is, $\mathfrak{R}_\lambda$ consists of those vectors y such that for some x, we have $H_\lambda x = y$. Since H_λ is one-to-one, we may "invert" it and consider the operator H_λ^{-1} which maps $\mathfrak{R}_\lambda$ onto $\mathfrak{H}$.

There are three possible cases:

1. $\mathfrak{R}_\lambda = \mathfrak{H}$;
2. $\mathfrak{R}_\lambda \neq \mathfrak{H}$ *but is dense in* $\mathfrak{H}$;
3. $\mathfrak{R}_\lambda \neq \mathfrak{H}$ *and is not dense in* $\mathfrak{H}$.

It may be shown that in case 1 the transformation H_λ^{-1} is bounded. It is easy to check the fact that in case 2 the transformation H_λ^{-1} is not bounded. In case 1 we say that λ *belongs to the resolvent set of* H, which set will be denoted by $\rho(H)$. If λ does not belong to the resolvent set, we shall say that λ belongs to the *spectrum* of H and we shall denote this set by $\sigma(H)$. We have defined the point spectrum of H. We shall refer to the set of values which fall under case 2 as the *continuous spectrum* of H. The set of values occurring in 3 is called the *residual spectrum* of H.

If H is symmetric, case 3 cannot occur; for if we have case 3, there exists a vector $y \neq 0$ which is orthogonal to all vectors $H_\lambda x$. Thus $(H_\lambda x, y) = 0$, or

$$(Hx, y) - \lambda(x, y) = 0,$$

for all x in $\mathfrak{H}$. But, since H is symmetric, $(Hx, y) = (x, Hy)$, this leads immediately to $Hy = \bar{\lambda}y$ where $\bar{\lambda}$ is the conjugate of λ. Since all eigenvalues of H are real, we have $\lambda = \bar{\lambda}$. Now, by definition, cases 1, 2, and 3 exclude the possibility of λ being in the point spectrum of H. Thus case 3 cannot arise for symmetric transformations. Also, it is not difficult to show, using the fact that (Hx, x) is a real number, that if λ is complex but not real, say, $\lambda = \alpha + \beta i$, $\beta \neq 0$, then H_λ^{-1} is bounded. Hence for λ not real, we have: λ is in the resolvent set of H.

We have proved, then, the following:

For a symmetric transformation H, every nonreal λ belongs to the resolvent set of H. If λ is real and belongs to the spectrum of H, it belongs either to the point spectrum or to the continuous spectrum.

If λ belongs to the continuous spectrum, owing to the unboundedness of H_λ^{-1}, it is easy to show (the reader should try it!) that there exist elements x with $\|x\| = 1$ and such that $\|Hx - \lambda x\|$ is arbitrarily small. Thus, from this point of view, the continuous spectrum represents a generalization of the point spectrum. Note that in the case of the point spectrum we replace "arbitrarily small" by "zero."

We give an example to show the scope of the phenomena in this situation. Consider the space L^2 on the unit interval, that is, the space of Lebesgue-measurable functions $x(t)$ for which $|x(t)|^2$ is integrable between 0 and 1, and let H be defined by $Hx = y$ where $y(t) = t \cdot x(t)$. At this moment, let us simplify our thinking by assuming that all functions are continuous, in which case the Lebesgue integral is identical with the integral discussed in an elementary calculus course. Making use of (14) we may see that H is symmetric; it is obviously linear. It is also easy to see from its definition that H is bounded, with $\|H\| = 1$.

Consider the question of the point spectrum. This resolves itself to the solution for $x(t)$ of the equation $t \cdot x(t) = \lambda x(t)$, where λ is fixed. The only possible solution—granting that our naive reasoning with continuous functions will not lead us astray —is a function $x(t)$ which is zero for all t except possibly for $t = \lambda$. The only such continuous function is the function f which is zero for all t. In other words, there is no λ in the point spectrum.

Whereas the point spectrum is empty, the continuous spectrum contains every number λ satisfying $0 \leq \lambda \leq 1$. In order to show this, it is sufficient to show that $H_\lambda^{-1} = (H - \lambda I)^{-1}$ is not bounded. Equivalently, it is sufficient to show that there exist functions x for which $\|x\| = 1$ and such that $\|H_\lambda x\|$ is arbitrarily small. The construction of such a function is easy. We take any $x(t)$ which is zero for all t not close to λ, has a high constant value for t near λ (the height is so chosen that $\|x\| = 1$), and rises from zero and descends to zero very abruptly on both sides of this constant value. Using (14) and the definition of the norm, $\|x\| = \sqrt{(x, x)}$, we see easily that $\|H_\lambda x\| = \|Hx - \lambda x\|$ is very small.

We are in a position to introduce with reference to this example the concepts which will be used in the statement of the spectral theorem in the general (bounded) case. Suppose that λ is a fixed number, $0 \leq \lambda \leq 1$, and consider the functions $x = x(t)$ which are zero to the right of λ: $x(t) = 0$ for $t \geq \lambda$. These form a linear manifold. If we consider not merely continuous functions but functions in L^2, the manifold is closed. Call it $\mathfrak{M}_\lambda$. Notice that $\{\mathfrak{M}_\lambda\}$ is an increasing family of manifolds; that is, if $\lambda_1 < \lambda_2$, then $\mathfrak{M}_{\lambda_1}$ is included in $\mathfrak{M}_{\lambda_2}$. Notice that $\mathfrak{M}_0$ contains only the vector 0 (usually written $\mathfrak{M}_\lambda = 0$) and $\mathfrak{M}_1 = \mathfrak{H}$.

Note that H transforms $\mathfrak{M}_\lambda$ into itself and its bound on $\mathfrak{M}_\lambda$ equals λ. Suppose we introduce the projection E_λ which is determined by $\mathfrak{M}_\lambda$ in the manner set forth in Section 3. Thus E_λ is a symmetric transformation satisfying $\|E_\lambda\| = 1$, $E_\lambda^2 = E_\lambda$, and $E_\lambda x = x$ if and only if x is in $\mathfrak{M}_\lambda$. Notice that if x is an arbitrary function, $E_\lambda x$ is the function obtained from x by suppressing $x(t)$ for t to the right of λ and replacing it by 0. If λ and μ are two real numbers with $\lambda < \mu$, $E_\mu x - E_\lambda x$ is the function y which equals 0 to the left of λ and to the right of μ and otherwise such that $y(t) = x(t)$. In other words, $y = (E_\mu - E_\lambda)x$ is obtained from x by "snipping off" $x(t)$ to the left† of λ and to the right of μ. Now we come to a very critical fact concerning the structure of symmetric transformations: If $\mu - \lambda$ is small, then Hy is approximately equal to λy, or, since $\mu - \lambda$ is small, to μy. In fact, the following may be proved for our example. Let ν be any number satisfying $\lambda \leq \nu \leq \mu$. Then

$$\|Hy - \nu y\| \leq (\mu - \lambda)\|y\|.$$

The underlying factor which makes the proof feasible is that in defining Hy, the integration from 0 to 1 may be replaced by an integration from λ to μ. This gives the above inequality immediately.

Having discussed this example at considerable length, let us proceed to a statement of the *results* (but not the proofs for them)

---

† It is not clear from the words whether "to the left of λ" means "for those t satisfying $t \leq \lambda$" or "for those t satisfying $t < \lambda$." In view of the fact that H has no point spectrum, the result is the same for both interpretations and we do not specify further what is intended. Similar difficulties occur subsequently and can be resolved by the same considerations.

in the general case. The transformation H is any bounded symmetric transformation. There may be found a family of linear manifolds $\mathfrak{M}_\lambda$, $-\infty < \lambda < \infty$, which has the following properties:

1. *For $\lambda < -\|H\|$, $\mathfrak{M}_\lambda = 0$; for $\lambda > \|H\|$, $\mathfrak{M}_\lambda = \mathfrak{H}$.*
2. *If $\lambda \leq \lambda'$, $\mathfrak{M}_\lambda$ is contained in $\mathfrak{M}_{\lambda'}$.*
3. *If x is in $\mathfrak{M}_\lambda$, Hx is in $\mathfrak{M}_\lambda$.*

We may transform these statements into statements concerning projections. We let E_λ represent the projection associated with the manifold pair $\{\mathfrak{M}_\lambda, \mathfrak{M}_\lambda^\perp\}$. Then E_λ, $-\infty < \lambda < \infty$, is a family of projections having the properties:

1'. *For $\lambda < -\|H\|$, $E_\lambda = O$; for $\lambda > \|H\|$, $E_\lambda = I$.*
2'. *If $\lambda \leq \lambda'$, $E_\lambda \leq E_{\lambda'}$.*
3'. *If $E_\lambda x = x$, then $E_\lambda H x = H x$.*

We define the expression $E_\lambda \leq E_{\lambda'}$ given in property 2' to mean the statement in 2. We may replace 3' by

3''. *For all x, $H E_\lambda x = E_\lambda H x$.*

The family E_λ which occurs above is called a *bounded resolution of the identity*. Every bounded symmetric transformation H gives rise to a bounded resolution of the identity. This resolution is essentially unique.† We note that E_λ is constant to the left of $\lambda = -\|H\|$ and also to the right of $\lambda = \|H\|$. Let λ, μ, ν be any three numbers satisfying $\lambda \leq \nu \leq \mu$ and let us think of $\mu - \lambda$ as being small. Then it may be shown that for any y of the form $y = (E_\mu - E_\lambda)x$, Hy is approximately equal to νy. In other words, $\|Hy - \nu y\|$ is small—in fact,

$$\|Hy - \nu y\| \leq (\mu - \lambda)\|y\|.$$

---

† The resolution can be made unique by requiring that E_λ be left continuous. This means that $\lim_{\epsilon \to 0} E_{\lambda-\epsilon} = E_\lambda$. Similar ambiguities come up in considering numerical-valued monotone-increasing functions which, for the purpose of Stieltjes integration of continuous functions, are not uniquely defined unless one requires one-sided continuity.

Now let $\lambda_0 \leq \lambda_1 \leq \cdots \leq \lambda_n$ be any $n + 1$ points for which $\lambda_0 < -\|H\|$ and $\lambda_n > \|H\|$. Let us write Δ_i for $\lambda_i - \lambda_{i-1}$; E_{Δ_i} for $E_{\lambda_i} - E_{\lambda_{i-1}}$; and λ_i' to represent any number satisfying

$$\lambda_{i-1} \leq \lambda_i' \leq \lambda_i, \qquad i = 1, \cdots, n.$$

Using properties 2 or 2' we find that for arbitrary vectors x and y and for $i \neq j$

$$(29) \qquad\qquad (E_{\Delta_i}x, E_{\Delta_j}y) = 0.$$

Since by 1',

$$(30) \qquad\qquad I = \sum_{i=1}^{n} E_{\Delta_i},$$

we have for any x

$$(31) \qquad\qquad x = \sum_{i=1}^{n} x_i$$

where $x_i = E_{\Delta_i}x$. Using (29), we can easily show that

$$(32) \qquad\qquad \|x\|^2 = \sum_{i=1}^{n} \|x_i\|^2.$$

Furthermore, since $E_{\Delta_i}x_i = x_i$, we have by a preceding paragraph

$$\|Hx_i - \lambda_i' x_i\| \leq \Delta_i \|x_i\|.$$

We stated in Section 3 that any bounded symmetric transformation H may be approximated in the norm by sums

$$\sum_{i=1}^{n} \alpha_i P_i$$

where the α_i are real and the P_i are projections. We are about to show this. Let ϵ be any positive number ($\epsilon > 0$), and let the λ_i be so chosen that $\Delta_i < \epsilon$. We shall show that

$$(33) \qquad\qquad \left\| H - \sum_{i=1}^{n} \lambda_i' E_{\Delta_i} \right\| < \epsilon.$$

The calculation contains a chain of steps. We note that a transformation T satisfies $\|T\| < \epsilon$ if and only if $\|Tx\| < \epsilon\|x\|$ for all x

in $\mathfrak{H}$. We have

(34)
$$\left\|\left(H - \sum_{i=1}^{n} \lambda_i' E_{\Delta_i}\right)x\right\|^2 = \left\|\sum_{i=1}^{n}(Hx_i - \lambda_i'x_i)\right\|^2$$

$$= \sum_{i=1}^{n} \|Hx_i - \lambda_i'x_i\|^2$$

$$\leq \sum_{i=1}^{n} \Delta_i^2\|x_i\|^2$$

$$\leq \epsilon^2 \sum_{i=1}^{n} \|x_i\|^2$$

$$= \epsilon^2\|x\|^2,$$

where we have used all the mathematical machinery of the preceding two pages.

It is clear to any one who has studied elementary Stieltjes integration that the sum

$$\sum_{i=1}^{n} \lambda_i' E_{\Delta_i}$$

is a type of Stieltjes integral. The integral may be defined in a way which is clear from the preceding, and we are thus led to the formula

(35)
$$H = \int_{-\infty}^{\infty} \lambda \, dE_\lambda,$$

where, by definition, the symbol on the right stands for limit obtained by the Δ-process of the finite sums

$$\sum_{i=1}^{n} \lambda_i' E_{\Delta_i}.$$

We note that although we have written down infinite limits of integration, they could have been replaced by any finite limits α and β with $\alpha < -\|H\|$ and $\beta > \|H\|$. This is characteristic of the bounded case. For the unbounded case, infinite limits (at least one!) in the integral (35) will be essential. Let us state now

THE SPECTRAL THEOREM (bounded case): *Let H be a bounded symmetric transformation. Then there exists a bounded resolution*

*of the identity E_λ which is essentially unique such that H is given
by the Stieltjes integral* (35). *Conversely, the transformation H
obtained in* (35) *from any bounded resolution of the identity is a
bounded symmetric transformation.*

The converse part is an immediate consequence of the facts
that any sum of the type

$$\sum_{i=1}^{n} \lambda_i' E_{\Delta_i}$$

is symmetric and any limit (in the norm) of symmetric transformations is symmetric.

Our discussion of the bounded case is complete. However,
before moving on, we should like to show how the completely
continuous case comes under the above theorem. In particular,
we shall show briefly how the manifolds $\mathfrak{M}_\lambda$ (equivalently, the
projections E_λ) are constructed.

Let H be completely continuous, and let λ be any real number.
Then $\mathfrak{M}_\lambda$ as defined in the present chapter is the smallest closed
linear manifold which includes all $\mathfrak{M}_{\lambda_i}$ of Section 4 (where λ_i
is an eigenvalue of H) for which $\lambda_i < \lambda$ (if one wishes one may
set $\lambda_i \leq \lambda$). Suppose, for example, that λ is positive. Suppose
that λ is not an eigenvalue of H. Then as λ increases from this
fixed value, $\mathfrak{M}_\lambda$ is constant until one reaches an eigenvalue λ_i.
As λ passes over the value λ_i, $\mathfrak{M}_\lambda$ jumps so as to include the
manifold of eigenvectors corresponding to λ_i. The jump consists
in the addition to $\mathfrak{M}_\lambda$ of the finite-dimensional manifold of
eigenvectors corresponding to λ_i. With these indications, it is
now straightforward to put the completely continuous case in
the frame of the more general situation.

One or two more observations should be made. Let us consider
the general bounded case. If E_λ is the resolution of the identity
of H and if λ is a fixed real number, then λ belongs to the point
spectrum if and only if

$$(36) \qquad \lim_{\epsilon \to 0} \mathfrak{M}_{\lambda+\epsilon} \neq \lim_{\epsilon \to 0} \mathfrak{M}_{\lambda-\epsilon},$$

where the limits are to be taken in a rather obvious sense which will not be made precise here. λ belongs to the resolvent set if and only if λ is the midpoint of some interval

$$\lambda - \epsilon \leq \mu \leq \lambda + \epsilon$$

with $\epsilon > 0$, such that $\mathfrak{M}_\mu$ is constant on this interval ($\mathfrak{M}_{\lambda-\epsilon} = \mathfrak{M}_\mu = \mathfrak{M}_{\lambda+\epsilon}$). The case "$\lambda$ is in the continuous spectrum" is obtained by exclusion of the two preceding cases.

Finally, note that we have asserted, without proof, the existence for every H of a bounded resolution of the identity E_λ having the requisite properties 1, 2, 3 and the critical approximation property summarized in the formula

$$\|Hy - \nu y\| \leq (\mu - \lambda)\|y\|$$

if $y = (E_\mu - E_\lambda)x$, $\lambda \leq \nu \leq \mu$. The proof of these critical facts is the crux of the entire problem and has not been touched here.

The above results are due to Hilbert. The form of Hilbert's results is completely different from that which we have given here, but it is nevertheless quite transparent for a reader with some sophistication. The results were published under the general title *Grundzüge einer allgemeinen Theorie der linearen Integralgleichungen* in the *Nachrichten der K. Gesellschaft der Wissenschaften zu Göttingen*. There were six communications in the same journal and under various special allied titles. Communication 1 in 1904 dealt with the completely continuous case of the preceding section. The results of the present section are given in communication 4 in 1906. All the communications were put together into a book bearing the title given above, which was published in 1912. This book is one of the most distinguished mathematical works of our century.

6. UNBOUNDED TRANSFORMATIONS

We may relieve the tension right from the start and assert that for the unbounded case the same result holds as for the bounded, providing that we replace the bounded resolution of the identity which is mentioned in the spectral theorem by an unbounded one. In other words, Eq. (35) is also valid for the unbounded case. However, having made these dramatic statements, we must perforce proceed much more delicately and more demurely. Indeed, our principal task will be to *define* the unbounded case.

Up to the present moment, all our transformations H have had the property that they were defined for every x in the Hilbert space. The exploitation of this fact leads to tremendous consequences. In particular, it allows us to define immediately the powers of H and polynomials in H. For example, H^2 is defined to be that transformation which carries x into Hy where $y = Hx$; thus $H^2x = H(Hx)$. If H is not defined for all vectors in $\mathfrak{H}$, then although for a given x, $y = Hx$ may exist, we may not blindly consider Hy. Thus, for such an H, the naive construction of the polynomials in H collapses.

Two remarks are in order here; one is that it is easy in the bounded case to define certain "analytic functions of H" such as $\exp H$ and $\sin H$. In fact, if H is not merely bounded but also symmetric, we may, without great effort, define arbitrary continuous functions of H. The second fact is that these continuous functions of H and also some discontinuous functions (the Baire functions) are at the base of the success we have in obtaining the spectral resolution of H. Thus, one of the most important factors leading to the structure theorem for H in the bounded case is completely absent in the unbounded case. We shall return to this feature of our problem in a few paragraphs.

We have observed that unbounded operators† are not defined for every x in $\mathfrak{H}$; let us give some examples. We begin with one which is suggestive but which will not be carried very far because of the difficulties inherent in a fine discussion—that of differentiation. Consider the space L^2 consisting of square integrable functions of the real variable t and where the inner product is given as in (14). Note that not every function $x(t)$ is differentiable and that, furthermore, if we set $Hx = x'$ (where $x'(t)$ denotes the derivative of $x(t)$), then H is not bounded. For example, if

---

† For us, the words "transformation" and "operator" are synonymous.

$x(t) = \sin nt$, then $x'(t) = n \cos nt$ and by taking n sufficiently large, it is clear that the ratio of $\|x'\|$ to $\|x\|$ can be made arbitrarily large. Thus, although differentiation is a linear transformation (as every calculus student learns), it is not bounded. This factor is essentially what makes the theory of differential equations a difficult subject.

For our next example, let us be somewhat more precise. Let $\mathfrak{H}$ consist of all square integrable functions $x = x(t)$ where the range of integration is the entire real axis. In this case we write $\mathfrak{H} = L^2(-\infty, \infty)$ to distinguish it from the previous space of functions which we can denote precisely by $L^2(0, 1)$. In $L^2(-\infty, \infty)$, consider the operator H defined by $Hx = y$ where $y(t) = t \cdot x(t)$. This operator is clearly symmetric (apply Eqs. (9) and (14)). It is also unbounded, for if $x(t)$ is the function which is zero everywhere except on the interval $n \leq t \leq n + 1$ where $x(t) = 1$, then $\|x\| = 1$ while $\|Hx\| > n$. The above example is important not only for its own sake; it also gives considerable insight into the general case. In particular, one may read Eq. (35) into it directly and see what the resolution of the identity is.

Having given some examples, let us define the object with which we are dealing. Let H represent a transformation defined for some but not necessarily all x in $\mathfrak{H}$. We require that the set $\mathfrak{D}$ on which H is defined be linear (that it contain $x + x'$ and αx whenever it contains x and x'). Furthermore, we require that $\mathfrak{D}$ be dense in $\mathfrak{H}$. The transformation H is assumed to be linear over its domain $\mathfrak{D}$. Now consider the set M of all pairs of vectors $\{y, z\}$ such that for all x in $\mathfrak{D}$ we have

(37) $$(Hx, y) = (x, z).$$

The set M contains at least one pair, namely, $\{0, 0\}$. Furthermore, the set cannot contain pairs $\{y, z\}$ and $\{y, z'\}$ with $z \neq z'$ since in that case $(x, z) = (x, z')$ for all x in the set $\mathfrak{D}$ which is dense in $\mathfrak{H}$, an impossibility. Finally, if M contains the pairs $\{y, z\}$ and $\{y', z'\}$, it also contains the pairs $\{\alpha y, \alpha z\}$ and $\{y + y', z + z'\}$. All this is clear. The preceding facts suggest that one may construct a transformation H^* defined as follows:

(38) $$H^*y = z.$$

The domain $\mathfrak{D}^*$ of H^* will then be the set of all y appearing in the pairs $\{y, z\}$ of M. The transformation H^* is called the *adjoint* of H. We may rewrite Eq. (37) in the form

$$(39) \qquad (Hx, y) = (x, H^*y),$$

where x is arbitrary in $\mathfrak{D}$ and y is arbitrary in $\mathfrak{D}^*$.

For bounded transformations, $\mathfrak{D}$ and $\mathfrak{D}^*$ coincide with $\mathfrak{H}$. For transformations in general, $\mathfrak{D}$ and $\mathfrak{D}^*$ are unrelated. A transformation H is said to be symmetric if $\mathfrak{D}$ is a subset of $\mathfrak{D}^*$ and if $Hx = H^*x$ for all x in $\mathfrak{D}$. It was J. von Neumann who studied in all details the structure of symmetric transformations and who discovered that, in going from the bounded to the unbounded case, a new phenomenon appears, namely that $\mathfrak{D}$ and $\mathfrak{D}^*$ need not be the same sets. In the present account, we shall speak only of the case $\mathfrak{D} = \mathfrak{D}^*$. A transformation H for which $\mathfrak{D} = \mathfrak{D}^*$ and such that $H = H^*$ is called *self-adjoint*. It is the self-adjoint transformations which we shall discuss in this section.

A few paragraphs ago we said that the key to the study of the structure of a bounded symmetric transformation H lay in the ability to construct functions of H, such as polynomial and other functions. Looking ahead to our final result, we can expect that unbounded self-adjoint transformations should "have functions" although the formation of these functions will undoubtedly be defined in a very sophisticated way. However, it may be that there are one or two very special functions of H which, by the dispensation of Providence and/or the stroke of a genius, (1) can be defined directly, that is, for which the above-mentioned difficulties can be circumvented; (2) turn out to be bounded; and (3) are such that the transformation H can be reconstructed from them. Thus if we write $K = f(H)$, we wish to be able to invert this, obtaining $H = f^{-1}(K)$.

There are two functions which have these properties and which can therefore be exploited for our purposes. Both of these functions were studied by von Neumann, who used the first to elaborate the main structure theorem and whose development of the second was sufficient to make the present program feasible for other authors capable of reading correctly between the lines.

The first function was

$$K = (H + iI)(H - iI)^{-1},$$

whose inverse is $H = i(K + I)(K - I)^{-1}$. Note that $i = \sqrt{-1}$.
This function is patterned after the numerical function $y = (x + i)(x - i)^{-1}$ which maps in a one-to-one manner the real axis on the unit circle in the complex plane from which the point $y = 1$ has been excluded. One difficulty (not deep) of the method is that K turns out to be a rotation in $\mathfrak{H}$ and not a symmetric transformation.[†] Thus von Neumann was led to the analysis of rotations—more properly called unitary transformations—for which the structure formula is like Eq. (35) except that the integrand is the complex quantity exp $(i\lambda)$. The second function is based on the transformation $K = (I + H^2)^{-1}$, some of whose properties may be correctly anticipated from its numerical antecedent $y = (1 + x^2)^{-1}$. In this case, the entire real axis is mapped onto the interval $0 < y \leq 1$. There are variants of this function which are useful; in particular,

$$y = x \cdot |x| \cdot (1 + x^2)^{-1}$$

maps the real axis in a one-to-one way on the open interval $-1 < y < 1$. Thus the associated transformation

$$K = H \cdot |H|(I + H^2)^{-1}$$

(to get it to behave is like taming a wild elephant) is a bounded symmetric transformation for which all the theory of the preceding chapter is immediately available.

Let us suppose for the sake of argument that we have a decent function $y = f(x)$ which maps the real axis in a one-to-one monotone-increasing way on a bounded open interval. Let us also suppose that, by some method, meaning can be assigned to the expression $K = f(H)$ which turns out to be a bounded symmetric transformation. Then if $E_\mu(K)$ is the resolution of the

---

[†] A rotation in Hilbert space is a linear transformation U which maps the space onto itself and which preserves norms: $\|Ux\| = \|x\|$. Alternatively, U is a rotation if $U^* = U^{-1}$.

identity associated with K, we have that $E_\lambda(H)$ is the resolution of the identity associated with H, where $E_\mu(K) = E_\lambda(H)$ and $\mu = f(\lambda)$. Thus, if we have

$$\mu_1 \leq \rho \leq \mu_2$$

where $\mu_2 - \mu_1$ is small, then as we have seen, K is approximately equal to ρI on the linear manifold determined by $E_{\mu_2}(K) - E_{\mu_1}(K)$. We have therefore that H is approximately equal to νI on this same manifold—that is, on the manifold $E_{\lambda_2}(H) - E_{\lambda_1}(H)$, where $\mu_i = f(\lambda_i)$ and $\rho = f(\nu)$.

The transformation H may be obtained by stretching, by the function $f(\lambda)$, the resolution of the identity of K so as to extend to infinity (to the right, left, or both) and proceeding to the calculation of the action of H with this new resolution of the identity and using Eq. (35). We may now explain a statement in Section 3 to the effect that an unbounded self-adjoint transformation may be considered as the limit of a sequence $\{H_n\}$ of bounded self-adjoint transformations. Suppose that in the integral representation (35) for the unbounded H, we integrate only over the interval $-n \leq \lambda \leq n$. We obtain thus a bounded symmetric transformation H_n defined (not on $\mathfrak{H}$ but) on the manifold or space associated with the projection $E_n - E_{-n}$. It is now apparent in which way H is the limit of the sequence of bounded transformations $\{H_n\}$. It is also clear that the sequence leading to H may be chosen in a great variety of ways.

Before terminating this section, we should like to return once more to the subject of functions of an operator H. For bounded operators, we have mentioned polynomials and suggested a few other types. We should like to indicate—however briefly—for its suggestive value, the general method for defining all functions of a self-adjoint transformation H. Before doing so, let us remind ourselves that there are several classes of functions with associated theories which are completely at variance with one another. Thus we have polynomials, analytic functions, continuous (or differentiable) functions, and measurable functions. The associated theories are algebra, complex function theory, real analysis, and measure theory. When we speak of functions of H, which do we have in mind? Some answers to this question (and we confine ourselves to bounded operators) are the following: For such an operator H, $f(H)$ is obviously defined for any polynomial $f(\lambda)$. We shall see shortly that for certain analytic functions $f(\lambda)$, the "analytic function of H," $f(H)$, is also defined. Now, for self-adjoint transformations H, it is possible to define the function $f(H)$ for any continuous function of H. This is a truly remarkable fact. This means that, in some sense, self-adjoint transformations fall under the domain of the theory of functions of a real variable whereas the general bounded transformation can only be considered in the framework of complex function theory. Let us indicate the meaning to be assigned to $f(H)$, where $f(\lambda)$ is a continuous function of the real variable λ. This is easy. We simply write

$$(40) \qquad\qquad f(H) = \int_{-\infty}^{\infty} f(\lambda)\, dE_\lambda.$$

Note that the integral is of the Riemann-Stieltjes type. This means that it is to be approximated by sums of the type

$$\sum_{i=1}^{n} f(\lambda_i') E_{\Delta_i}$$

where Δ_i represents the interval $[\lambda_{i-1}, \lambda_i]$ and where λ_i' is any point in that interval. The facts as to the approximation can be proved easily from elementary properties of continuous functions (on finite intervals) and from the orthogonality properties of the resolution of the identity E_λ. In particular, note that the approximation is in the norm of the vector space of all bounded linear transformations discussed in Section 3. Equation (40) may seem somewhat high-handed. The reader should convince himself that this formula is consistent with the older and more naive equation given for polynomials. In particular, he should investigate $f(\lambda) = \lambda^2$ (consider, for example, the point spectrum).

For a self-adjoint transformation H, we may define $f(H)$ not merely for continuous functions $f(\lambda)$ but also for measurable†

---

† The definition of a measurable function of H was first given by von Neumann in 1931. The notion of a projection-valued measure which eliminated bilinear forms and the Lebesgue-Stieltjes integral was introduced later by the author.

functions of H. We cannot say here what a measurable function of H is. However, we may suggest one easy example: Suppose $f(\lambda)$ equals 1 for $\lambda \leq \mu$ where μ is a fixed constant and $f(\lambda) = 0$ for $\lambda > \mu$. Then it is not difficult to convince oneself that $f(H) = E_\mu$. Thus every projection E_μ in the resolution of the identity of H is a function (in general, discontinuous) of H. Let us close this section with one further thought. The mapping from the functions of a real variable $f(\lambda)$ into the operators $f(H)$ is an algebraic homomorphism from the set of H measurable functions onto the set of functions of H. This means that "sums go into sums and products into products." Note also that the function $f(\lambda) = \lambda$ goes into H (Eq. (35)), and that $f(\lambda) = 1$ goes into I. This mapping together with its associated homomorphism is called the *operational calculus* of H.

7. SOME EXTENSIONS

We shall describe briefly some developments in analysis which have followed the discoveries of Section 6. As things stood there, the last word had been said on the structure of a self-adjoint transformation. An obvious question concerned the structure of an arbitrary transformation, not necessarily self-adjoint. A second question concerned the structure of an entire class of transformations. In this latter category, we might consider the class of transformations $f(H)$ with a fixed H given in Eq. (40). There is not much to be said here since the structure of the class $\{f(H)\}$ is completely determined by the structure of H. We do note, however, that $\{f(H)\}$ is closed under the operations of addition and multiplication (as well as scalar multiplication), and hence it is an algebra. Very characteristically, it is a commutative algebra. This suggests the analysis of algebras of transformations. These algebras are either commutative or noncommutative. It is obvious that the two corresponding theories will be quite different from one another. In this section, by deliberate choice, we shall not consider the noncommutative case.

Let us return to the first question, that of determining the structure of an arbitrary bounded linear transformation H. It turns out that it is of little assistance to know that H operates on a Hilbert space $\mathfrak{H}$. We obtain as much information if we assume merely that H is defined on a *Banach space*—that is, a normed space satisfying (11a), (11b), and (11c) and which is complete in that norm (in the sense explained in Section 2).

Suppose then that $\mathfrak{B}$ is a Banach space and H is a bounded linear transformation in $\mathfrak{B}$. We note first that if $\mathfrak{B}$ is finite-dimensional, the structure problem is completely solved, the result being contained in the *Jordan canonical form* for a matrix.† We note next that the general problem in an arbitrary Banach space is quite beyond us insofar as a complete solution is concerned. Numerous examples reveal a discouragingly large class of phenomena which we are not as yet in a position to classify. However, a beginning can be made.

The direction of this general beginning is rather clear. We have seen that the resolution of the identity is the key to the structure of self-adjoint transformations. This resolution consists of projections P (thus satisfying $P^2 = P$) which are functions of H and hence commute with $H : PH = HP$. A short argument will show that if H is arbitrary and if P is a projection which commutes with H, then the space $\mathfrak{B}$ may be expressed as the sum of two disjoint subspaces (closed linear manifolds) $\mathfrak{M}$ and $\mathfrak{N}$ such that Hx is in $\mathfrak{M}$ when x is in $\mathfrak{M}$ and Hx is in $\mathfrak{N}$ when x is in $\mathfrak{N}$. The entire discussion of this point is exactly as in Section 3 except for the fact that here $\mathfrak{N}$ is not $\mathfrak{M}^{\perp}$ and that P is not symmetric. It is clear then that the first step in studying the structure of H consists in determining all projections P which commute with H. Better (and easier) yet, is to determine all projections which are functions of H.

It was F. Riesz who first indicated that one may consider the notion of an analytic function of an arbitrary transformation.

---

† The Jordan canonical form for matrices is derived in any treatise on finite-dimensional vector spaces. See, for example, P. R. Halmos' book by that name, Van Nostrand, Princeton, second edition, 1958. It may also be found in the mimeographed notes of a course given twenty years ago by the author, some copies of which are still available and may be obtained from him on request.

The procedure is as follows: If H is a bounded transformation in $\mathfrak{B}$, one considers the resolvent set $\rho(H)$ consisting of the complex numbers λ such that $(H - \lambda I)^{-1}$ exists and is bounded. This set turns out to be open, while its complement $\sigma(H)$ is closed; the latter is also bounded. The transformation $(\zeta I - H)^{-1}$ exists on $\rho(H)$ and is a continuous function of ζ. We may integrate the function along any rectifiable curve C in the complex plane which lies wholly in $\rho(H)$. In particular, we may consider the integral

$$(41) \qquad P = \frac{1}{2\pi i} \int_C (\zeta I - H)^{-1} \, d\zeta$$

for a simple closed curve C lying in $\rho(H)$. The classic Cauchy theory asserts that if we consider the analogous integral with H replaced by a scalar operator αI, then the value of the integral is O if α lies outside C and is I if α lies inside C. In any case, the integral satisfies $P^2 = P$. If H is arbitrary, in general, P is not O or I but is an intermediate projection since one may prove also here that it satisfies $P^2 = P$. The projection P *reduces* H, and one of the subspaces associated with P has the property, rapidly expressed, that the spectrum of H for this subspace lies inside C. If the spectrum of H lies wholly inside C, $P = I$, and only then.

Riesz essentially considered expressions of the form

$$(42) \qquad f(H) = \frac{1}{2\pi i} \int_C f(\zeta)(\zeta I - H)^{-1} \, d\zeta,$$

where $f(\zeta)$ is analytic in a region including C but where $\sigma(H)$ lies entirely within C. It may thus be seen from our discussion that there are two variables at our disposal, the function $f(\zeta)$ and the curve C. We see† from these brief statements that we may develop an entire theory of analytic functions of an arbitrary transformation in a Banach space and that this theory gives initial results towards the determination of the structure of such a transformation.

---

† The theory of the reducibility of linear transformations in Banach spaces was given by the author in 1942. It includes a complete analysis of the properties of the operator P in (41).

At first glance, the methods used here do not seem to have a sharp enough edge to secure the full story as given either in Section 5 or Section 6 for a self-adjoint transformation H. We recall that such transformations have their spectrum on the real axis. Let us suppose that there are two gaps in this spectrum, that is, two points λ_1 and λ_2 with $\lambda_1 < \lambda_2$ which do *not* belong to the spectrum. Then an easy computation shows that the integral (41) for a simple curve C which crosses the real axis only at λ_1 and λ_2 yields

$$P = E_{\lambda_2} - E_{\lambda_1},$$

where E_λ is the resolution of the identity of H. Thus the method allows us to determine the value of E at all points λ which lie in the resolvent set.

A refinement of the method allows us to obtain the value of E_λ even for points λ in the spectrum. More precisely, if the curve C is chosen as above and if one uses the function

$$f(\zeta) = (\zeta - \lambda_1)(\lambda_2 - \zeta)$$

in the integral (42), one obtains a function $f(H)$ whose range is precisely the manifold† associated with $E_{\lambda_2} - E_{\lambda_1}$. Given this manifold, the projection may be reconstructed in a trivial way as indicated in Section 3. Note that the integral (42) is improper in that case since C does not lie exclusively in the resolvent set (C contains λ_1 and λ_2). The convergence of the integral is a simple matter to treat. (The reader should note that the convergence is in terms of the norm or bound of the transformation. There are many topologies which may be introduced into the space of transformations, and the one which we invoke is the simplest of all.) This method, which is valid from the start for both the bounded and the unbounded case, seems from many

---

† As frequently happens, the possible existence of a point spectrum challenges the veracity of the statements one wishes to make. To obviate this annoyance, one "eliminates" the point spectrum at the outset by "pulling out" of $\mathfrak{H}$ the linear manifold $\mathfrak{M}$ on which the transformation H has pure point spectrum and considering the structure of H on $\mathfrak{M}^\perp$. Having done this one has a situation in which $\mathfrak{M} = 0$ and $\mathfrak{M}^\perp = \mathfrak{H}$.

points of view to be the most rapid for developing the spectral theorem.

Let us turn now to the consideration of rings of transformations. As we have said above, we shall consider commutative rings only, and we shall assume these rings to be complete in the metric of the norm $\|H\|$ associated with any transformation H. We see in passing that if H and K are two bounded transformations in the ring, then $(HK)x = H(Kx)$ and also

$$\|(HK)x\| = \|H(Kx)\| \leq \|H\| \cdot \|Kx\| \leq \|H\| \cdot \|K\| \cdot \|x\|.$$

Thus we have the inequality (by the definition of $H \cdot K$)

$$(43) \qquad \|H \cdot K\| \leq \|H\| \cdot \|K\|.$$

The object $\mathfrak{A}$ with which we are dealing is a class of linear transformations which constitutes a complete normed vector space (hence a Banach space) and which admits multiplication. Such objects are called *normed rings* or (more frequently) *Banach algebras*. There is little advantage to be gained in the treatment of these algebras if we consider them algebras of transformations, and we shall therefore consider that we are dealing with an abstract algebra, that is, one in which the elements H are not assumed to have properties and structure in addition to those which appear on the surface in the algebra.

Our point of view at this moment is somewhat as follows. If H is self-adjoint and bounded, and if $f(\lambda)$ is any continuous complex-valued function of λ, then the class of functions $f(H)$ defined in Eq. (40) is a normed ring in which the operations are very similar to the operations in the ring of the $f(\lambda)$. The phrase "very similar" means that there is a homomorphic mapping of one on the other and that by a suitable "adjustment," this homomorphism can be made into an isomorphism. The question now arises whether any normed ring is homomorphic or isomorphic to a ring of—or to *the* ring of *all*—continuous functions on a suitable topological space. It should be noted that we have several questions here and that the sharpest one is: When is a normed ring algebraically and metrically isomorphic to the ring of all continuous functions on a suitable topological space? Let

us make some observations of a topological nature. The word
"suitable" turns out to be interpreted as *compact;* and every continuous function on a compact space is bounded. For a bounded
function f on a compact space S, the "natural" norm is $\|f\|$,
defined to be the maximum value of $|f(\lambda)|$ on S.

Let us state right away what some of the results are. Every
normed ring is homomorphic to a ring of continuous functions
on a compact space S. It is algebraically isomorphic to this
ring of functions if and only if the normed ring has no radical.†
Simple abstract conditions may be given which imply that a
normed ring satisfying them is algebraically and metrically
isomorphic to the ring of all continuous functions on some
compact space S. If H is bounded and self-adjoint, then the
ring of all polynomials in H and their limits satisfies the conditions of the previous theorem, and is therefore equivalent to
the ring of all continuous functions on a compact space. Every
ring of continuous functions may be extended to the ring of all
bounded Baire functions (obtained from the continuous functions by taking pointwise limits).

The spectral theorem now appears much more transparent.
The space S associated to the ring generated by H consists of
the points in the spectrum of H, viz., a compact subset of the
real axis. The function of H which corresponds to E_μ is a Baire
function, namely the function which equals 1 to the left of μ
and 0 to the right of μ. Just as the function $f(\lambda) = \lambda$ can be
approximated uniformly on any compact set by step functions
(that is, functions which are constant on an interval), so can
H, the correspondent of $f(\lambda) = \lambda$, be approximated uniformly
in the manner exhibited in (33).

The discussion of the proof of the statements of the preceding
paragraphs would involve deeply the fields of algebra and
topology. For this reason the subject-matter belongs to the

---

† Without attempting to define the notion of radical, let us say that it
consists of elements a for which $a^n = 0$ for some n or for which $(\lambda a)^n \longrightarrow 0$
for all λ as $n \longrightarrow \infty$. To say that a ring has no radical is to say that the
only element with this property is $a = 0$.

domain of topological algebra. We cannot enter here into these matters for lack of time, of space, and, most important, of energy on the part of a more than patient reader.†

---

† However, if our patient reader, rather than lacking energy, lacks patience with our all too gentle and ineffective approach and wishes to get at the cortex of these matters, we recommend to him any book on Banach algebras—for example, that of L. H. Loomis, *Abstract Harmonic Analysis*, Van Nostrand, Princeton, 1953.

PRELIMINARIES TO FUNCTIONAL ANALYSIS

Casper Goffman

Functional analysis, briefly, is that branch of mathematics in which elements of a given class of functions are considered to be points of an appropriate infinite-dimensional space. In this way, various theories of functions, real and complex, are seen from either a geometric or point-set theoretic view, often achieving new levels of unification.

1. FIXED-POINT THEOREMS

1. The subject may be introduced by means of fixed-point theorems and their application to differential and integral equations. Consider first the integral equation

$$(1) \qquad f(x) = \int_a^b \phi(x, y) f(y) \, dy,$$

where ϕ is continuous on the closed square $[a, b] \times [a, b]$. The problem is to show that there is a continuous f on $[a, b]$ which satisfies Eq. (1). Observe that for every continuous g, defined on $[a, b]$, the function

$$h(x) = \int_a^b \phi(x, y)g(y) \, dy$$

is continuous, so that the righthand side of Eq. (1) defines a mapping which takes every continuous g into a continuous h. It becomes apparent that the proof that a solution to Eq. (1) exists amounts to the same thing as a proof that there is a continuous function which is taken into itself by this mapping, i.e., a function which remains fixed under the mapping. Thus, if functions are themselves considered as points of a space, we are interested in a statement regarding the existence of fixed points for certain kinds of mappings.

2. We consider a more familiar situation. Let R be the real number continuum, and let f be a mapping which takes R into itself. Then, for every $x \in R$, $f(x) \in R$. We suppose there is a positive constant $k < 1$ such that, for every $x \in R$, $y \in R$,

$$(2) \qquad |f(x) - f(y)| \leqq k|x - y|.$$

We remark, in passing, that (2) implies that f is continuous.

We shall prove that f has a fixed point. Moreover, we shall prove that the fixed point is unique. For this purpose, we may start with any $x \in R$. We shall use the notation $x_0 = x$, $x_1 = f(x_0)$, $x_2 = f(x_1)$, and, for every $n = 1, 2, \cdots$, $x_{n+1} = f(x_n)$. Now, for every n,

$$|f(x_{n+1}) - f(x_n)| \leqq k|f(x_n) - f(x_{n-1})|$$

since $x_{n+1} = f(x_n)$ and $x_n = f(x_{n-1})$. Similarly,

$$|f(x_n) - f(x_{n-1})| \leqq k|f(x_{n-1}) - f(x_{n-2})|$$

so that

$$|f(x_{n+1}) - f(x_n)| \leqq k^2|f(x_{n-1}) - f(x_{n-2})|.$$

By continuing this process, we finally obtain

$$|f(x_{n+1}) - f(x_n)| \leqq k^n|f(x) - x|.$$

Having proved this, let $\epsilon > 0$. There is an N such that

$$\sum_{n=N}^{\infty} k^n |f(x) - x| < \epsilon.$$

Thus, if $n > N$, $m > 0$, then

$$|x_n - x_{n+m}| = |f(x_{n-1}) - f(x_{n+m+1})|$$

$$\leqq \sum_{s=n-1}^{n+m-2} |f(x_{s+1})| - f(x_s)|$$

$$\leqq \sum_{s=n-1}^{n+m-2} k^s |f(x) - x|$$

$$\leqq \sum_{n=N}^{\infty} k^n |f(x) - x| < \epsilon.$$

The sequence $\{x_n\}$ thus satisfies the Cauchy criterion for convergence. Let $X = \lim\limits_{n \to \infty} x_n$. Then

$$X = \lim_{n \to \infty} x_n = \lim_{n \to \infty} f(x_n) = f(X).$$

Hence, $X = f(X)$.

Suppose Y is such that $f(Y) = Y$. Then

$$|f(X) - f(Y)| \leqq k|X - Y|.$$

Since $k < 1$, this implies $X = Y$. We have thus proved:

If f is a function on the reals to the reals and if there is a k with $0 < k < 1$ such that for every x, y, with $x \neq y$,

$$|f(x) - f(y)| \leqq k|x - y|$$

then there is one and only one X such that $f(X) = X$.

3. We note that the only properties of the real numbers used in the above proof are the triangle property of the absolute value and the Cauchy criterion for convergence. The above theorem accordingly holds under much more general circumstances which we now describe, taking the opportunity to discuss the notion of metric space and related ideas.

A *metric space* consists of a set S together with a real function d defined on $S \times S$ such that

(a) *for every* $x \in S$, $y \in S$, $d(x, y) > 0$ *if* $x \neq y$ *and* $d(x, y) = 0$ *if* $x = y$;

(b) $d(x, y) = d(y, x)$,

(c) *for every* $x \in S$, $y \in S$, $z \in S$, $d(x, z) \leqq d(x, y) + d(y, z)$.

It is clear that the real numbers, with $d(x, y) = |x - y|$, form a metric space.

The n-dimensional space E_n, of points $x = (x_1, \cdots, x_n)$, with distance

$$d(x, y) = [\sum_{i=1}^{n} (x_i - y_i)^2]^{1/2},$$

is also a metric space. It is only necessary to verify that

$$d(x, z) \leqq d(x, y) + d(y, z).$$

This will follow from the Cauchy-Schwarz inequality, which says that for any real numbers $a_1, \cdots, a_n$,

$$|\sum_{i=1}^{n} a_i b_i| \leqq [\sum_{i=1}^{n} a_i^2]^{1/2}[\sum_{i=1}^{n} b_i^2]^{1/2}.$$

We prove this inequality by first noting the trivial fact that for any reals A, B we have

$$2|AB| \leqq A^2 + B^2.$$

Letting

$$A = \frac{|a_i|}{[\sum_{i=1}^{n} a_i^2]^{1/2}} \quad \text{and} \quad B = \frac{|b_i|}{[\sum_{i=1}^{n} b_i^2]^{1/2}},$$

we obtain

$$\frac{2|a_i b_i|}{[\sum_{i=1}^{n} a_i^2]^{1/2} [\sum_{i=1}^{n} b_i^2]^{1/2}} \leqq \frac{a_i^2}{\sum_{i=1}^{n} a_i^2} + \frac{b_i^2}{\sum_{i=1}^{n} b_i^2}.$$

By adding for $i = 1, \cdots, n$ we obtain the inequality

$$\frac{2 \sum\limits_{i=1}^{n} |a_i b_i|}{[\sum\limits_{i=1}^{n} a_i^2]^{1/2} [\sum\limits_{i=1}^{n} b_i^2]^{1/2}} \leqq 2$$

and the Cauchy-Schwarz inequality is proved.

Now

$$\sum_{i=1}^{n} (a_i + b_i)^2 \leqq \sum_{i=1}^{n} |a_i + b_i| \, |a_i| + \sum_{i=1}^{n} |a_i + b_i| \, |b_i|$$

$$\leqq [\sum_{i=1}^{n} (a_i + b_i)^2]^{1/2}[\sum_{i=1}^{n} a_i^2]^{1/2}$$

$$+ [\sum_{i=1}^{n} (a_i + b_i)^2]^{1/2}[\sum_{i=1}^{n} b_i^2]^{1/2}$$

by the Cauchy-Schwarz inequality. Hence, multiplying by $[\sum\limits_{i=1}^{n} (a_i + b_i)^2]^{-1/2}$, we obtain

$$[\sum_{i=1}^{n} (a_i + b_i)^2]^{1/2} \leqq [\sum_{i=1}^{n} a_i^2]^{1/2} + [\sum_{i=1}^{n} b_i^2]^{1/2}.$$

Letting $a_i = y_i - x_i$ and $b_i = z_i - y_i$ for $i = 1, \cdots, n$, we obtain

$$[\sum_{i=1}^{n} (z_i - x_i)^2]^{1/2} \leqq [\sum_{i=1}^{n} (z_i - y_i)^2]^{1/2} + [\sum_{i=1}^{n} (y_i - x_i)^2]^{1/2},$$

or $d(z, x) \leqq d(x, y) + d(y, z)$.

If we consider any numbers $p, q > 1$ for which $1/p + 1/q = 1$ we can prove the inequality

$$|ab| \leqq \frac{|a|^p}{p} + \frac{|b|^q}{q}$$

which is a generalization of

$$|ab| \leqq \frac{a^2}{2} + \frac{b^2}{2}.$$

By following the lines of the above proof we obtain as a generalization of the Cauchy-Schwarz inequality, the Hölder inequality

$$\sum_{i=1}^{n} |a_i b_i| \leq [\sum_{i=1}^{n} |a_i|^p]^{1/p} \cdot [\sum_{i=1}^{n} |b_i|^q]^{1/q}.$$

From the Hölder inequality follows the Minkowski inequality

$$[\sum_{i=1}^{n} |a_i + b_i|^p]^{1/p} \leq [\sum_{i=1}^{n} |a_i|^p]^{1/p} + [\sum_{i=1}^{n} |b_i|^p]^{1/p}.$$

In other words, for every $p > 1$, E_n is a metric space with metric

$$d(x, y) = [\sum_{i=1}^{n} |x_i - y_i|^p]^{1/p}.$$

E_n is also a metric space for the case $p = 1$ with metric

$$d(x, y) = \sum_{i=1}^{n} |x_i - y_i|.$$

These results extend immediately to infinite sequences. Consider, for example, the set of all sequences $x = \{x_n\}$ for which

$$\sum_{n=1}^{\infty} x_n^2 < \infty,$$

and designate this set by l_2. We shall prove that l_2 is a vector space. A real vector space is a set X which is an abelian group, the group operations being written additively as $(x, y) \longrightarrow x + y$. Moreover, there is scalar multiplication of $x \in X$ by $a \in R$ written as $(a, x) \longrightarrow ax$ satisfying the laws $a(bx) = (ab)x$, $(a + b)x = ax + bx$, $a(x + y) = ax + ay$, and $1x = x$. If θ is the group identity, it is easy to prove that $0x = \theta$ for every $x \in X$. Now, E_n is a vector space with operations

$$(x_1, \cdots, x_n) + (y_1, \cdots, y_n) = (x_1 + y_1, \cdots, x_n + y_n)$$

and

$$a(x_1, \cdots, x_n) = (ax_1, \cdots, ax_n).$$

It is not immediate that l_2 with the analogous operations is a vector space. In order to prove that it is, we suppose $(x_1, x_2, \cdots)$

and $(y_1, y_2, \cdots)$ are in l_2. Then

$$\sum_{i=1}^{\infty} x_i^2 < \infty \qquad \text{and} \qquad \sum_{i=1}^{\infty} y_i^2 < \infty.$$

For every n,

$$[\sum_{i=1}^{n} (x_i + y_i)^2]^{1/2} \leqq [\sum_{i=1}^{n} x_i^2]^{1/2} + [\sum_{i=1}^{n} y_i^2]^{1/2}.$$

It follows that

$$[\sum_{i=1}^{\infty} (x_i + y_i)^2]^{1/2} \leqq [\sum_{i=1}^{\infty} x_i^2]^{1/2} + [\sum_{i=1}^{\infty} y_i^2]^{1/2}$$

so that

$$\sum_{i=1}^{\infty} (x_i + y_i)^2 < \infty \qquad \text{and} \qquad (x_1 + y_1, x_2 + y_2, \cdots) \in l_2.$$

It now follows easily that l_2 is a vector space. In similar fashion every l_p, $p > 1$ is a vector space. In vector spaces, metrics may be defined in terms of norms related to the vector-space operations. A norm in a vector space X is a nonnegative real function, written as $\|x\|$, satisfying the condition

$$\|\theta\| = 0, \qquad \|x\| > 0$$

if $x \neq \theta$,

$$\|ax\| = |a|\,\|x\|, \quad \text{and} \quad \|x + y\| \leqq \|x\| + \|y\|.$$

The corresponding metric is defined by $d(x, y) = \|x - y\|$. The above remarks constitute the main part of a proof that l_2 is a normed vector space with norm

$$\|x\| = [\sum_{i=1}^{\infty} x_i^2]^{1/2}.$$

Similarly, every l_p, $p \geqq 1$ is a normed vector space with norm

$$\|x\| = [\sum_{i=1}^{\infty} |x_i|^p]^{1/p}.$$

Other important examples of normed vector spaces have functions on continua, rather than sequences, as elements.

Perhaps the simplest example is the space C of continuous functions on the closed interval $[0, 1]$, where if $x = x(t)$ then

$$\|x\| = \max \{|x(t)| : t \in [0, 1]\}.$$

It is easily verified that C is a normed vector space. There are also the L_p spaces, $p \geq 1$. A function x is in L_p, $p \geq 1$, if

$$\int_0^1 |x(t)|^p \, dt < \infty.$$

The analogues of the Hölder and Minkowski inequalities remain valid here, the proofs being essentially the same as for the finite-dimensional case. The L_p spaces are accordingly normed vector spaces with norm

$$\|x\| = \left[\int_0^1 |x(t)|^p \, dt \right]^{1/p}.$$

4. The other property of the real number system needed for the proof of the fixed-point theorem is that every sequence $\{x_n\}$ which satisfies the Cauchy criterion converges to a number x. For a metric space X, this property is called *completeness*. In X a sequence $\{x_n\}$ is called a *Cauchy sequence* if for every $\epsilon > 0$ there is an N such that $m, n > N$ implies

$$d(x_m, x_n) < \epsilon.$$

An $x \in X$ is called a *limit* of $\{x_n\}$ if for every $\epsilon > 0$ there is an N such that $n > N$ implies

$$d(x, x_n) < \epsilon.$$

A metric space X is called *complete* if every Cauchy sequence in X has a limit.

That the real numbers form a complete metric space will be assumed without proof. The l_p spaces, $p \geq 1$, are complete metric spaces. We prove this for the case $p = 1$. Let $\{x^{(m)}\}$ be a Cauchy sequence in l_1. Then $x^{(m)} = \{x_n^{(m)}\}$ for every $m = 1$, $2, \cdots$, where

$$\sum_{n=1}^{\infty} |x_n^{(m)}| < \infty,$$

and for every $\epsilon > 0$ there is an N such that $\mu, \nu > N$ implies

$$\|x^{(\mu)} - x^{(\nu)}\| = \sum_{n=1}^{\infty} |x_n^{(\mu)} - x_n^{(\nu)}| < \epsilon.$$

It follows that for every n the sequence $\{x_n^{(m)}\}$ is a Cauchy sequence of real numbers. Let

$$x_n = \lim_{m \to \infty} x_n^{(m)}.$$

We first show that $\{x_n\} \in l_1$. Since $\{x^{(m)}\}$ is a Cauchy sequence it is bounded in l_1, i.e., there is an M such that

$$\sum_{n=1}^{\infty} |x_n^{(m)}| \leq M$$

for every m. Then, for every N,

$$\sum_{n=1}^{N} |x_n| \leq M$$

so that

$$\sum_{n=1}^{\infty} |x_n| \leq M$$

and $\{x_n\} \in l_1$. It remains for us to show that $x = \{x_n\}$ is the limit of $\{x^{(m)}\}$ in l_1. Let $\epsilon > 0$. Choose N so that $\mu > N$ implies

$$\sum_{n=1}^{\infty} |x_n^{(N)} - x_n^{(\mu)}| < \epsilon.$$

Now, for every k,

$$\sum_{n=1}^{k} |x_n^{(N)} - x_n| = \lim_{\mu \to \infty} \sum_{n=1}^{k} |x_n^{(N)} - x_n^{(\mu)}| \leq \epsilon,$$

so that

$$\sum_{n=1}^{\infty} |x_n^{(N)} - x_n| \leq \epsilon.$$

This proves that l_1 is complete.

This proof is a prototype for various completeness proofs. Thus if we wish to show that a given metric space of functions is complete we may proceed as follows: For a given Cauchy sequence $\{f_n\}$, obtain first a function f to which either $\{f_n\}$ or a subsequence of $\{f_n\}$ converges in a pointwise sense (perhaps everywhere except at a set which may be considered as being negligible). Next show that $f \in X$. Finally show that $\{f_n\}$ converges to f in the space X.

The normed vector space C of continuous functions on $[0, 1]$ with

$$\|x\| = \max \{|x(t)| : t \in [0, 1]\}$$

is complete. This follows since a Cauchy sequence $\{x^{(m)}\}$ is merely one which converges uniformly. Let

$$x = \lim_{m \to \infty} x^{(m)}.$$

But the limit of a uniformly convergent sequence of continuous functions is continuous. Hence $x \in C$. Finally, it is clear that

$$\lim_{m \to \infty} \|x - x^{(m)}\| = 0.$$

The continuous functions also form a normed vector space with the norm

$$\|x\| = \int_0^1 |x(t)| \, dt.$$

This space K is not complete. For example, let $x^{(m)}$ be defined by

$$x^{(m)}(t) = \begin{cases} 0, & 0 \leq t \leq \dfrac{1}{2} - \dfrac{1}{m}; \\[2mm] mt + 1 - \dfrac{m}{2}, & \dfrac{1}{2} - \dfrac{1}{m} \leq t \leq \dfrac{1}{2}; \\[2mm] 1, & \dfrac{1}{2} \leq t \leq 1. \end{cases}$$

The reader may verify that $\{x^{(m)}\}$ is a Cauchy sequence in K, but that there is no continuous function to which $\{x^{(m)}\}$ converges. A similar remark may be made for the space R of Riemann integrable functions on $[0, 1]$ with the norm

$$\|x\| = \int_0^1 |x(t)| \, dt,$$

although a more subtle Cauchy sequence must be found in order for it not to have a Riemann integrable limit. This lack of completeness is perhaps the main reason for the need of another concept of integral. The Lebesgue integral is obtained by removing the defect. Indeed, the classical process' of completing the rationals by taking as new objects, the reals, equivalence classes of Cauchy sequences, applies to any metric space. Accordingly, every metric space may be imbedded as a dense subset in a complete metric space. In this way, the Lebesgue integrable functions may be obtained as the completion of the space R or even of the space K. Albeit this manner of defining Lebesgue integrability is simple and elegant, it is only fair to mention that it gives insufficient information regarding the properties of the objects of the completed space, and that other ways of defining the Lebesgue integral remain preferable.

5. We may now state the fixed-point theorem.

THEOREM 1: *If X is a complete metric space, and f is a mapping of X into itself such that there is a k, where $0 < k < 1$, so that for every x, $y \in X$ we have $d(f(x), f(y)) \leqq k \, d(x, y)$, then the mapping f has exactly one fixed point.*

The proof, which is essentially the same as for the real numbers, is left as an exercise for the reader.

6. There are other, more difficult fixed-point theorems. However, even the one we are considering has interesting applications.

Let ϕ be a continuous real function defined on the square $[a, b] \times [a, b]$, and let g be continuous on $[a, b]$. We consider the Fredholm-type equation

$$(3) \qquad f(x) = \lambda \int_a^b \phi(x, y) f(y) \, dy + g(x)$$

of which Eq. (1) is a special case. To say that, for a given λ, Eq. (3) has a solution is the same as saying that the mapping defined by the righthand side of Eq. (3) has a fixed point. Call the mapping Φ. Every continuous f is taken into a function Φf that is also continuous. We thus have a mapping Φ from the space C of continuous functions on $[a, b]$ into C. We metrize C with the norm

$$\|f\| = \max \{|f(x)| : x \in [a, b]\}.$$

We first show that Φ is continuous on C, i.e.,

$$\lim_{n \to \infty} \|f_n - f\| = 0 \quad \text{implies} \quad \lim_{n \to \infty} \|\Phi f_n - \Phi f\| = 0.$$

This follows since, for every x,

$$|\Phi f(x) - \Phi h(x)| = \left| \lambda \int_a^b \phi(x, y) f(y) \, dy - \lambda \int_a^b \phi(x, y) h(y) \, dy \right|$$

$$\leq |\lambda| \int_a^b |\phi(x, y)| \, |f(y) - h(y)| \, dy$$

$$\leq |\lambda| M(b - a) \max \{|f(y) - h(y)| : y \in [a, b]\},$$

where $M = \max \{|\phi(x, y)| : x, y \in [a, b]\}$. Hence,

$$\|\Phi f - \Phi h\| \leq |\lambda| M(b - a) \|f - h\|.$$

This last inequality shows that Φ satisfies the condition of Theorem 1 for

$$|\lambda| < 1/[M(b - a)].$$

Accordingly, Eq. (3) has one and only one solution for every such λ.

As a second example, we consider the differential equation

$$dy/dx = f(x, y).$$

Suppose f is defined on an open connected set R in the plane, and is continuous and satisfies a Lipschitz condition on y in R, i.e., there is an L such that, whenever (x, y_1), $(x, y_2) \in R$,

$$|f(x, y_1) - f(x, y_2)| \leq L|y_1 - y_2|.$$

Let $(x_0, y_0) \in R$. We shall show that there is an $\eta > 0$ such that there is a unique $y = y(x)$, with $y_0 = y(x_0)$ which satisfies the differential equation for

$$x \in [x_0 - \eta, x_0 + \eta].$$

We first note that this is equivalent to y satisfying the integral equation

$$y(x) = y_0 + \int_{x_0}^x f(t, y(t)) \, dt.$$

Let Δ be a circle which, together with its boundary, is contained in R and whose center is (x_0, y_0). Let

$$|f(x, y)| \leq M$$

on Δ. Let $\delta > 0$ be such that the rectangle

$$I \times J = [x_0 - \delta, x_0 + \delta] \times [y_0 - \delta M, y_0 + \delta M]$$

is contained in Δ and such that $L\delta < 1$. Let C be the space of continuous functions on I with values in J, with the metric

$$d(y_1, y_2) = \max \{|y_1(x) - y_2(x)| : x \in I\}.$$

This is a complete metric space. The mapping Φ defined by

$$\Phi y(x) = y_0 + \int_{x_0}^{x} f(t, y(t))\, dt$$

is a mapping of C into C satisfying the conditions of Theorem 1. In order to see this, we first let $y \in C$ and $|x - x_0| \leq \delta$. Then

$$|\Phi y(x) - y_0| = \left| \int_{x_0}^{x} f(t, y(t))\, dt \right| \leq M\delta,$$

so that, since Φy is continuous, $\Phi y \in C$. Now, for every $x \in I$,

$$|\Phi y_1(x) - \Phi y_2(x)| \leq \int_{x_0}^{x} |f(t, y_1(t)) - f(t, y_2(t))|\, dt$$
$$\leq L \int_{x_0}^{x} |y_1(t) - y_2(t)|\, dt \leq L\delta \max \{|y_1(x) - y_2(x)| : x \in I\}.$$

In other words, $d(\Phi y_1, \Phi y_2) \leq L\delta\, d(y_1, y_2)$. Since $L\delta < 1$, Theorem 1 shows that the differential equation $dy/dx = f(x, y)$ has a unique solution curve passing through (x_0, y_0) which is defined at least in a neighborhood of (x_0, y_0).

2. COMPACT SPACES

1. A second method of functional analysis has as its germ the so-called Bolzano-Weierstrass theorem. This says that a bounded infinite set on a closed interval $[a, b]$ has at least one limit point in $[a, b]$. A related fact is the Borel covering theorem which says that if a closed interval $[a, b]$ is covered by a collection of open sets, then a finite number of open sets from the collection covers $[a, b]$. A topological space X is called compact if it has the property of this last theorem, i.e., if for every covering of X by a collection of open sets, a finite number of open sets from the collection covers X. A set $S \subset X$ is a compact subset of X if every collection of open sets in X which covers S has a finite subcollection which covers S.

In a metric space X, an open sphere of center x and radius r is the set

$$\sigma(x, r) = \{y : d(x, y) < r\}.$$

Then $S \subset X$ is compact if every collection of open spheres covering S has a finite subcollection covering S. It is easily seen that, in a metric space, a set S is compact if and only if every infinite subset $T \subset S$ has a limit point in S, i.e., there is an $x \in S$ such that, for every

$$r > 0, \sigma(x, r)$$

contains an infinite number of points of T.

In regard to compactness in metric spaces, the notion of total boundedness is central. A set S in a metric space X is totally bounded if for every $\epsilon > 0$ there is a finite set $T_\epsilon \subset S$ such that for every $x \in S$ there is a $y \in T_\epsilon$ with $d(x, y) < \epsilon$. It is not hard to prove that in a metric space X a set S is compact if and only if it is closed and totally bounded.

2. We now pass to the problem of characterizing compact subsets of special spaces. We first consider the space C of continuous functions on a closed interval $[a, b]$ with the standard metric. A set $S \subset C$ is said to be equicontinuous if for every $\epsilon > 0$ there is a $\delta > 0$ such that $|x - y| < \delta$ and $f \in S$ implies

$$|f(x) - f(y)| < \epsilon.$$

THEOREM 2 (Arzela-Ascoli): *A set $S \subset C$ is compact if and only if it is closed in C, uniformly bounded, and equicontinuous.*

Proof: We sketch the sufficiency proof. Since S is uniformly bounded there is an M such that for every $f \in S$ and $x \in [a, b]$,

$|f(x)| \leqq M$. For every m, let

$$J_1^m = \left[a, \, a + \frac{b-a}{m} \right],$$

and

$$J_k^m = \left(a, \, a + \frac{k(b-a)}{m} \right], \qquad k = 2, \, \cdots, \, m.$$

For every n, let S_{mn} consist of all functions which are constant on each J_k^m and whose value is of the form j/n, where $\left| \dfrac{j}{n} \right| \leqq M$, on each J_k^m. The sets S_{mn} are all finite. By the equicontinuity of S, for every $\epsilon > 0$, there are m and n such that, for every $f \in S$, there is a $g \in S_{mn}$ with

$$|f(x) - g(x)| < \epsilon/2,$$

for every $x \in [a, b]$. It follows that there is a finite $T_\epsilon \subset S$ such that, for every $f \in S$, there is a $g \in T_\epsilon$ with

$$|f(x) - g(x)| < \epsilon$$

for every $x \in [a, b]$. Thus, S is totally bounded. It follows from the assumption that S is closed that it is compact.

For the necessity, suppose S is compact. If S is not closed, there is a sequence $\{f_n\}$ in S which converges uniformly to a function $f \notin S$, so that S is not compact. If S is not bounded, there is a sequence $\{f_n\}$ in S which does not converge and has no convergent subsequence, so that S is not compact. If S is not equicontinuous, there is a sequence $\{f_n\}$ in S which is not equicontinuous. It is easily shown, however, that a uniformly convergent sequence of continuous functions on a closed interval is equicontinuous. Hence, if S is compact, then it is equicontinuous.

3. This theorem may be used to prove that the differential equation

$$dy/dx = f(x, y),$$

with $f(x, y)$ continuous in a connected open set R, has a solution curve passing through every

$$(x_0, \, y_0) \in R,$$

in a neighborhood of (x_0, y_0). Let Δ be a circle, center (x_0, y_0), which together with its boundary is contained in R. By the Weierstrass approximation theorem (see the paper by Stone in this present volume), there is a sequence of polynomials $\{P_n(x, y)\}$ which converges uniformly to $f(x, y)$ in a circle Δ', containing Δ, also contained in R. There is an M such that

$$|f(x, y)| \leqq M$$

and, for every n,

$$|P_n(x, y)| \leqq M$$

for every $(x, y) \in \Delta$. Since, as is easily verified, each $P_n(x, y)$ satisfies a Lipschitz condition, the differential equation

$$dy/dx = P_n(x, y)$$

has a unique solution y_n defined on an interval

$$I = [x_0 - \delta, x_0 + \delta]$$

with values in

$$J = [y_0 - M\delta, y_0 + M\delta],$$

where $I \times J \subset \Delta$, with $y_n(x_0) = y_0$. Let C, metrized in the standard way, be the space of continuous functions on I, with values in J, such that $y(x_0) = y_0$. Let $S \subset C$ be the closure in C of the set whose elements are $y_1, y_2, \cdots$. Then S is closed and bounded in C. We show that $\{y_n\}$ is equicontinuous. For this, we note that for every $x \in I$,

$$y_n(x) = y_0 + \int_{x_0}^{x} P_n(t, y_n(t)) \, dt,$$

so that

$$|y_n(x_1) - y_n(x_2)| \leqq \int_{x_1}^{x_2} |P_n(t, y_n(t))| \, dt \leqq M|x_1 - x_2|.$$

Hence, for every $\epsilon > 0$,

$$|x_1 - x_2| < \frac{\epsilon}{M} \quad \text{implies} \quad |y_n(x_1) - y_n(x_2)| < \epsilon,$$

for every n, proving the equicontinuity of $\{y_n\}$. S is also equicontinuous for, otherwise, S would have a sequence $\{z_n\}$ such that, for some $\epsilon > 0$, and every $\eta > 0$, there would be x_1, x_2 with $|x_1 - x_2| < \eta$, and an n, such that

$$|z_n(x_1) - z_n(x_2)| > 3\epsilon.$$

For every n, there is a y_m with

$$|z_n(x) - y_m(x)| < \epsilon$$

for every x. It follows that for every $\eta > 0$, there would be x_1, x_2, with $|x_1 - x_2| < \eta$, and an n, such that

$$|y_n(x_1) - y_n(x_2)| < \epsilon,$$

contradicting the equicontinuity of $\{y_n\}$. It now follows that S is compact, so that the sequence $\{y_n\}$ has a subsequence, which we also designate by $\{y_n\}$, which converges uniformly to a $Y \in S$. Obviously, $Y(x_0) = y_0$. We prove that for every $x \in I$,

$$Y(x) = y_0 + \int_{x_0}^{x} f(t, Y(t)) \, dt.$$

We note that

$$Y(x) = \lim_{n \to \infty} y_n(x).$$

Moreover, since $P_n(x, y)$ converges uniformly to $f(x, y)$ on Δ, it follows that

$$\int_{x_0}^{x} f(t, Y(t)) \, dt = \lim_{n \to \infty} \int_{x_0}^{x} P_n(t, Y(t)) \, dt = \lim_{n \to \infty} \int_{x_0}^{x} P_n(t, y_n(t)) \, dt,$$

since

$$\left| \int_{x_0}^{x} P_n(t, Y(t)) \, dt - \int_{x_0}^{x} P_n(t, y_n(t)) \, dt \right| \leqq \int_{x_0}^{x} |P_n(t, Y(t))$$

$$- P_n(t, y_n(t))| \, dt \leqq \int_{x_0}^{x} |P_n(t, Y(t)) - f(t, Y(t))| \, dt$$

$$+ \int_{x_0}^{x} |f(t, Y(t)) - f(t, y_n(t))| \, dt + \int_{x_0}^{x} |f(t, y_n(t)) - P_n(t, y_n(t))| \, dt,$$

and each of the three terms on the righthand side converges to zero as n increases, the first and third by the uniform convergence of $\{P_n\}$ to f, and the second by the uniform continuity of f and the uniform convergence of $\{y_n\}$ to Y. This completes the proof.

4. As a second example, we consider the metric space A of holomorphic functions in the unit disk

$$U = \{z : |z| < 1\}.$$

Our metric here will be the one which corresponds to the topology of uniform convergence on compact subsets of U. It may be defined as follows: Let f, $g \in A$, let

$$U_n = \left\{ z : |z| < 1 - \frac{1}{n} \right\},$$

and let

$$d_n(f, g) = \max \{ |f(z) - g(z)| : z \in U_n \}.$$

Finally, let

$$d(f, g) = \sum_{n=1}^{\infty} \frac{1}{2^n} \frac{d_n(f, g)}{1 + d_n(f, g)}.$$

It can be verified that A is a complete metric space, and that $\{f_n\}$ converges to f in this metric if and only if $\{f_n\}$ converges uniformly to f on every compact subset of U. In order to be able to characterize compact sets in A, we need the

LEMMA 1: *If $S \subset A$ is uniformly bounded on U_n, then it is equicontinuous on U_n.*

Proof: Let M be such that $|f(z)| \leqq M$ for every $f \in S$ and $z \in U_n$. Let $m > n$ and let

$$K = \{z : |z| = 1 - 1/m\}.$$

Now, for z_1, $z_2 \in U_n$,

$$f(z_1) = \frac{1}{2\pi i} \int_K \frac{f(\zeta)}{\zeta - z_1} \, d\zeta$$

and

$$f(z_2) = \frac{1}{2\pi i} \int_K \frac{f(\zeta)}{\zeta - z_2} \, d\zeta,$$

so that

$$|f(z_1) - f(z_2)| \leqq \frac{1}{2\pi} \int_K \left| \frac{f(\zeta)}{\zeta - z_1} - \frac{f(\zeta)}{\zeta - z_2} \right| |d\zeta| \leqq \frac{mnM}{m - n} |z_1 - z_2|.$$

Hence, for every $\epsilon > 0$, if

$$|z_1 - z_2| \leqq \frac{m - n}{mnM} \epsilon$$

then $|f(z_1) - f(z_2)| < \epsilon$ for every $f \in S$ so that S is equicontinuous.
   We now prove the

   THEOREM 3: *A set* $S \subset A$ *is compact if and only if it is closed
in* A *and uniformly bounded on every compact subset of* U.

   Proof: The necessity is obvious. For the sufficiency, let $\{f_m\}$
be any sequence in S. By Lemma 1 and the assumption that
$\{f_m\}$ is uniformly bounded on U_n it follows that $\{f_m\}$ is equicontinuous on U_n, for every n. Let $\{f_{2,m}\}$ be a subsequence of $\{f_m\}$
which converges uniformly on U_2; $\{f_{3,m}\}$ a subsequence of $\{f_{2,m}\}$
which converges uniformly on U_3, and so on. It follows that
$\{f_{m,m}\}$ is a subsequence of $\{f_m\}$ which converges uniformly on
each $U_n, n = 1, 2, \cdots$. In other words, every sequence in S has
a Cauchy subsequence, and since S is closed in A, it follows that
S is compact.

   Compact subsets of A are called *normal families*. They play an
important role in the theory of functions of a complex variable.
   5. The most important applications of compactness are to the
calculus of variations. For this purpose a companion notion,
lower semicontinuity, is needed.
   We consider a real function f defined on a closed interval
$[a, b]$. f is said to be lower semicontinuous at $x \in [a, b]$ if for
every $\epsilon > 0$ there is a $\delta > 0$ such that $y \in [a, b]$ and $|x - y| < \delta$
implies

$$f(y) > f(x) - \epsilon.$$

Upper semicontinuity may be defined similarly, but will not be
needed here. We prove:

If f *is a real function defined on a closed interval* $[a, b]$, *and* f *is
lower semicontinuous at every* $x \in [a, b]$, *then* f *has an absolute
minimum in* $[a, b]$, *i.e., there is an* $x_0 \in [a, b]$ *such that*

$$f(x) \geqq f(x_0)$$

for every $x \in [a, b]$.

Proof: We first note that f has a lower bound on $[a, b]$. For, suppose that for every n there is an $x_n \in [a, b]$ such that $f(x_n) < -n$. Then $\{x_n\}$ has a convergent subsequence converging to an $x_0 \in [a, b]$. For every $\delta > 0$, there is an x_n with

$$|x_n - x_0| < \delta$$

and

$$f(x_n) < f(x_0) - 1.$$

This contradicts the lower semicontinuity of f at x_0. Since f has a lower bound, it has a greatest lower bound L on $[a, b]$. For every n, there is an $x_n \in [a, b]$ with

$$f(x_n) < L + 1/n.$$

Now, $\{x_n\}$ has a convergent subsequence converging to an $x_0 \in [a, b]$. Suppose $f(x_0) = L + k$, $k > 0$. Then, for every $\delta > 0$, there is an x_n with $1/n < k/2$ and $|x_n - x_0| < \delta$. But

$$f(x_n) < f(x_0) - k/2$$

contradicts the lower semicontinuity of f at x_0. Hence

$$f(x_0) = L \quad \text{and} \quad f(x) \geqq f(x_0)$$

for every $x \in [a, b]$.

With no essential changes in this proof, we obtain

THEOREM 4. *If S is a compact metric space and f is lower semicontinuous on S, then f has an absolute minimum on S.*

By a curve C, we shall understand a continuous mapping of the closed interval $[0, 1]$ into E_n. For convenience, we consider only E_2. A curve, then, is given by a pair $x(t)$, $y(t)$ of continuous real functions. Let

$$T : 0 = t_0 < t_1 < \cdots < t_n = 1$$

be a partition of $[0, 1]$ and let

$$\lambda(f, T) = \sum_{i=1}^{n} \{[x(t_i) - x(t_{i-1})]^2 + [y(t_i) - y(t_{i-1})]^2\}^{1/2}.$$

The length of C is defined as

$$l(C) = \sup \{\lambda(f, T) : T\}.$$

The following analogue, due to Hilbert, of the Arzela-Ascoli theorem is valid.

THEOREM 5 (Hilbert): *If S is a set of curves of finite length, which lie in a bounded region of the plane, and whose lengths form a bounded set, then if S is closed it is compact.*

We omit the proof, which is much like that of Theorem 2, but add only that we have considered S to be a metric space with metric

$$d(C_1, C_2) =$$
$$\max \{\{[x_1(t) - x_2(t)]^2 + [y_1(t) - y_2(t)]^2\}^{1/2} : t \in [0, 1]\}.$$

In the calculus of variations, the following type of problem arises. Let

$$K = \{z : |z| < R\}$$

and let $\mathfrak{C}$ be a closed set of curves in K, the set of whose lengths is bounded. Then $\mathfrak{C}$ is compact. Let $f(x, y, x', y')$ be continuous in the four variables and of class C'' in x', y' for each $(x, y) \in K$. Moreover, suppose f satisfies the homogeneity condition

$$f(x, y, kx', ky') = f(x, y, x', y').$$

This homogeneity is necessary for line integrals of f to be independent of the representation of the curve along which the integration is performed. With certain further restrictions on f, it can be shown that

$$I(C) = \int_0^1 f(x(t), y(t), x'(t), y'(t))\, dt$$

is a lower semicontinuous functional on $\mathfrak{C}$. It follows from the compactness of $\mathfrak{C}$ that there is a $C_0 \in \mathfrak{C}$ for which $I(C)$ has an absolute minimum.

3. HILBERT SPACES AND BANACH SPACES

1. A complete normed vector space is called a *Banach space*. The most important Banach spaces are the space C of continuous functions and the space L_2 of functions which are square integrable in the sense of Lebesgue. For convenience, we consider only real functions on [0, 1]. The norm for C is taken as

$$\|f\| = \max\{|f(x)| : x \in [0, 1]\},$$

and the norm for L_2 is taken as

$$\|f\| = \left\{\int_0^1 |f(x)|^2 \, dx\right\}^{1/2}.$$

Although these norms are chosen mainly for their intuitive naturalness, there are other compelling reasons for their choice. In particular, if we ask for a norm on the space of continuous functions which makes it a Banach space, and which is such that $\|1\| = 1$ and such that

$$\|f\| \geq \|g\|$$

whenever f and g obey $|f(x)| \geq |g(x)|$ for all x, then we must be content with the usual maximum norm. Comparable characterizations can be given for the L_2 norm.

2. The space L_2 is of special interest. It has geometrical properties which are much like those of finite-dimensional euclidean space. For example, it satisfies the parallelogram law

$$\|f + g\|^2 + \|f - g\|^2 = 2\|f\|^2 + 2\|g\|^2.$$

However, the main fact about L_2 is that the norm may be defined in terms of a scalar product, and this leads to a useful notion of orthogonality. We recall that if $f, g \in L_2$ then

$$\int_0^1 |fg| \, dx \leq \|f\| \, \|g\|,$$

so that

$$\int_0^1 f(x)g(x) \, dx$$

exists and is finite. We call the number

$$\int_0^1 f(x)g(x)\,dx$$

the *scalar product* of f and g, and write

$$(f,\,g)\;=\;\int_0^1 f(x)g(x)\,dx.$$

It is easily verified that the scalar product satisfies the conditions

(a) *for every* $f,\,g \in L_2$, $(f,\,g)\,=\,(g,\,f)$,

(b) *for every* $f,\,g \in L_2$ *and real* a, $(af,\,g)\,=\,a(f,\,g)$,

(c) *for every* $f,\,g,\,h \in L_2$, $(f,\,g+h)\,=\,(f,\,g)\,+\,(f,\,h)$,

(d) *for every* $f \in L_2$, $(f,\,f)\,\geqq\,0$, *and* $(f,\,f)\,=\,0$ *if and only if* $f(x)\,=\,0$ *almost everywhere.*

It follows from (a), (b), (c) that the scalar product also satisfies $(f,\,ag)\,=\,a(f,\,g)$ and

$$(g+h,\,f)\;=\;(g,\,f)\,+\,(h,\,f).$$

The scalar product is thus a symmetric bilinear functional. Observe that

$$\|f\|\,=\,(f,\,f)^{1/2}, \qquad \|f\|\,\geqq\,0, \qquad \|f\|\,=\,0$$

if and only if $f(x)\,=\,0$ almost everywhere. It is thus convenient to consider as the elements of L_2 the equivalence classes of square integrable functions, where $f \sim g$ if $f(x)\,=\,g(x)$ almost everywhere.

The space L_2 is a special case of a type of Banach space called *Hilbert space.* A real Hilbert space $\mathfrak{H}$ is a vector space over the reals for which a bilinear functional $(f,\,g)$ is defined satisfying the above conditions (a), (b), (c), (d), and which is complete in the metric corresponding to the associated norm $\|f\|\,=\,(f,\,f)^{1/2}$. Another example of a Hilbert space is the space l_2 of sequences $\{x_n\}$ for which

$$\sum_{n=1}^{\infty} x_n^2\,<\,\infty,$$

with scalar product

$$(x, y) = \sum_{n=1}^{\infty} x_n y_n.$$

We shall consider only infinite-dimensional spaces, i.e., those for which there is no finite set $f_1, \cdots, f_n$ whose linear combinations generate the space. A metric space is called *separable* if it has a countable dense set. If $\mathfrak{H}_1$, $\mathfrak{H}_2$ are infinite-dimensional separable Hilbert spaces, it can be shown that there is a one-one mapping ϕ of $\mathfrak{H}_1$ onto $\mathfrak{H}_2$ such that

$$\phi(af + bg) = a\phi(f) + b\phi(g), \quad \text{and} \quad (\phi(f), \phi(g)) = (f, g),$$

for every $f, g \in \mathfrak{H}_1$ and real a, b. The spaces L_2 and l_2 are separable, so that they are concrete realizations of the same abstract system.

3. Let $\mathfrak{H}$ be a separable Hilbert space. Elements $x, y \in \mathfrak{H}$ are called *orthogonal* if $(x, y) = 0$; x is called *normal* if $\|x\| = 1$. A set $S \subset \mathfrak{H}$ is called an *orthonormal set* if every $x \in S$ is normal and every $x, y \in S$ are orthogonal. An orthonormal set S is called *complete* if it is not contained in a larger orthonormal set. In a separable Hilbert space, every orthonormal set is countable. For if S is such a set, then for every $x, y \in S$,

$$\|x - y\| = (x - y, x - y)^{1/2} = (\|x\|^2 + \|y\|^2)^{1/2} = 2^{1/2}.$$

Let T be a countable dense set. To every $x \in S$, mate an $x' \in T$ such that

$$\|x - x'\| < 2^{-1/2}.$$

This mating is one-one between S and a subset of T, so that S is countable. Complete orthonormal sets may be obtained by applying the Schmidt orthogonalization process to a countable dense set. For nonseparable Hilbert spaces, their existence follows by using Zorn's lemma.

Let $\mathfrak{H}$ be a separable Hilbert space and let $x_1, x_2, \cdots$ be a complete orthonormal set in $\mathfrak{H}$. Let $x \in \mathfrak{H}$. The numbers (x, x_n) may be called the *Fourier coefficients* of x, and the formal expression

$$\sum_{n=1}^{\infty} (x, x_n)x_n$$

the *Fourier expansion* of x. Consider the subspace $\mathfrak{H}_n$ of $\mathfrak{H}$ generated by $x_1, \cdots, x_n$. Let $x \in \mathfrak{H}$. We find the point in $\mathfrak{H}_n$ of shortest distance from x. For this purpose, consider

$$\|x - \sum_{i=1}^{n} a_i x_i\|.$$

$$\|x - \sum_{i=1}^{n} a_i x_i\|^2 = (x - \sum_{i=1}^{n} a_i x_i, x - \sum_{i=1}^{n} a_i x_i)$$

$$= \|x\|^2 - \sum_{i=1}^{n} (x, x_i)^2 + \sum_{i=1}^{n} (a_i - (x, x_i))^2.$$

This expression is evidently smallest when $a_i = (x, x_i)$, $i = 1, \cdots, n$. Since

$$\|x - \sum_{i=1}^{n} (x, x_i)x_i\|^2 \geqq 0,$$

this also proves Bessel's inequality,

$$\|x\|^2 \geqq \sum_{i=1}^{n} (x, x_i)^2.$$

Now, let

$$y_n = \sum_{i=1}^{n} (x, x_i)x_i.$$

Then

$$\|y_{n+p} - y_n\|^2 = \sum_{i=n+1}^{n+p} (x, x_i)^2,$$

and it follows from Bessel's inequality that $\{y_n\}$ is a Cauchy sequence. Let $y = \lim_{n \to \infty} y_n$ in $\mathfrak{H}$. Clearly, $(y, x_i) = (x, x_i)$, for every i. In other words, $(y - x, x_n) = 0$, for every n, so that, since $\{x_n\}$ is a complete orthonormal set, $y = x$. Hence

$$\sum_{n=1}^{\infty} (x, x_n)x_n$$

converges in $\mathfrak{H}$ to x. Moreover, since

$$\|x - \sum_{i=1}^{n} (x, x_i)x_i\|^2 = \|x\|^2 - \sum_{i=1}^{n} (x, x_i)^2,$$

it follows that

$$\|x\|^2 = \sum_{n=1}^{\infty} (x, x_n)^2.$$

We combine these facts in the following theorem:

THEOREM 6. *If $\mathfrak{H}$ is a separable Hilbert space and $\{x_n\}$ is a complete orthonormal set in $\mathfrak{H}$, then for every $x \in \mathfrak{H}$,*

$$\|x\| = \sum_{n=1}^{\infty} (x, x_n)^2$$

and the series

$$\sum_{n=1}^{\infty} (x, x_n)x_n$$

converges in $\mathfrak{H}$ to x.

4. We now prove another geometrical fact about $\mathfrak{H}$. Let $K \subset \mathfrak{H}$ be a closed subspace. We show that for every $x \in \mathfrak{H}$, $x = y + z$, where $y \in K$ and z is orthogonal to every element in K. Moreover, this decomposition is unique.

Proof: Let $x \in \mathfrak{H}$. Let $d = \inf \{\|y - x\| : y \in K\}$. There is $\{y_n\}$ in K with

$$d = \lim_{n \to \infty} \|x - y_n\|.$$

For every n, m we have

$$\left\| x - \frac{y_n + y_m}{2} \right\| \geqq d.$$

Then, by the parallelogram law,

$$\|y_n - y_m\|^2 \leqq 2\|x - y_n\|^2 + 2\|x - y_m\|^2 - 4d^2,$$

and it follows that $\{y_n\}$ is a Cauchy sequence. Let

$$y = \lim_{n \to \infty} y_n.$$

Then $y \in K$ and $\|x - y\| = d$. We need only show that

$$(x - y, u) = 0,$$

for every $u \in K$. Now,

$$\|x - y\|^2 \leqq \|x - y - au\|^2 = \|x - y\|^2 - 2a(x - y, u) + a^2\|u\|^2,$$

for every a. Setting $a\|u\|^2 = (x - y, u)$, we have $(x - y, u)^2 \leqq 0$. For the uniqueness, let $x = y' + z'$ be another decomposition. Then

$$y + z = y' + z' \quad \text{implies} \quad y - y' = z - z'$$

so that

$$\|y - y'\|^2 = (z - z', y - y') = 0,$$

and $y = y', z = z'$.

5. This decomposition allows us to define an important class of linear operators in a Hilbert space. First, we make some general statements concerning operators in Banach spaces. A linear operator on X into Y is a mapping U of X in Y such that

$$U(ax + by) = aU(x) + bU(y)$$

for every $x, y \in X$ and real a, b. U is *continuous* if

$$\lim_{n \to \infty} \|x - x_n\| = 0$$

implies

$$\lim_{n \to \infty} \|U(x) - U(x_n)\| = 0.$$

It is easy to see that U is continuous if and only if it is continuous at $x = \theta$. A linear operator is called *bounded* if the set

$$\{U(x) : \|x\| = 1\} \text{ is bounded.}$$

The norm of a bounded operator is defined by

$$\|U\| = \sup \{\|U(x)\| : \|x\| = 1\}.$$

It is easy to prove that the continuous linear operators are precisely the bounded ones. Consider the case of a bounded linear operator on a Hilbert space $\mathfrak{H}$ into $\mathfrak{H}$. A is called *symmetric* if for every $x, y \in \mathfrak{H}$, $(Ax, y) = (x, Ay)$. Let A be a symmetric bounded linear operator,

$$m = \inf \{(Ax, x) : \|x\| = 1\}, \quad \text{and} \quad M = \sup \{(Ax, x) : \|x\| = 1\}.$$

It can be shown (see Riesz-Nagy, p. 227) that

$$\|A\| = \max \{|m|, |M|\}.$$

Let $\mathfrak{H}$ be a Hilbert space and $\mathfrak{M}$ a closed subspace of $\mathfrak{H}$. For every $x \in \mathfrak{H}$, let $P_{\mathfrak{M}}x$, the projection of x in $\mathfrak{M}$, be the component of x, in the above decomposition, which is in $\mathfrak{M}$. Thus, $x - P_{\mathfrak{M}}x$ is orthogonal to every element in $\mathfrak{M}$. Then

$$P_{\mathfrak{M}}(ax + by) = aP_{\mathfrak{M}}x + bP_{\mathfrak{M}}y,$$

so that $P_{\mathfrak{M}}$ is linear. Moreover,

$$\|x\|^2 = \|P_{\mathfrak{M}}x + (x - P_{\mathfrak{M}}x)\|^2 = \|P_{\mathfrak{M}}x\|^2 + \|x - P_{\mathfrak{M}}x\|^2$$

so that, for every x,

$$\|P_{\mathfrak{M}}x\| \leqq \|x\|,$$

and $P_{\mathfrak{M}}$ is a bounded operator. Furthermore, $P_{\mathfrak{M}}$ is *idempotent*, i.e., $P_{\mathfrak{M}}^2 = P_{\mathfrak{M}}$. For,

$$P_{\mathfrak{M}}^2 x = P_{\mathfrak{M}}(P_{\mathfrak{M}}x) = P_{\mathfrak{M}}x.$$

Finally, for every $x, y \in \mathfrak{H}$,

$$(P_{\mathfrak{M}}x, y) = (P_{\mathfrak{M}}x, P_{\mathfrak{M}}y) = (x, P_{\mathfrak{M}}y),$$

so that $P_{\mathfrak{M}}$ is symmetric. Thus $P_{\mathfrak{M}}$ is an idempotent, symmetric, bounded linear operator. It is called the *projection* in $\mathfrak{M}$. Conversely, every idempotent, symmetric, bounded linear operator P is a projection, the corresponding subspace being the set $\mathfrak{M}$ of fixed points of P. For, let $x \in \mathfrak{M}$. Then

$$x = Px + (x - Px).$$

First, $Px \in \mathfrak{M}$, since $Px = P^2x \in \mathfrak{M}$. We need only show that $x - Px$ is orthogonal to $\mathfrak{M}$. Let $y \in \mathfrak{M}$. Then

$$(x - Px, y) = (x - Px, Py) = (Px - P^2x, y)$$
$$= (Px - Px, y) = 0.$$

An operator A is called *positive* if, for every

$$x \in \mathfrak{H}, (Ax, x) \geqq 0.$$

Projections are positive. Indeed,

$$(Px, x) = (P^2x, x) = (Px, Px) \geqq 0.$$

For operators A and B, $A \geqq B$ if $A - B$ is positive. If $\mathfrak{M} \supset \mathfrak{N}$, then $P_{\mathfrak{M}} - P_{\mathfrak{N}}$ is positive. For, it is easy to verify that $P_{\mathfrak{M}} - P_{\mathfrak{N}}$ is a projection on that subspace of $\mathfrak{M}$ which is the orthogonal complement of $\mathfrak{N}$.

6. Projections are important in the spectral decomposition of an operator A. For the finite-dimensional case, we recall that a symmetric linear operator A may be decomposed as

$$A = \sum_{i=1}^{k} \lambda_i P_i$$

where the λ_i are the characteristic numbers and the P_i are the projections in the corresponding invariant subspaces. A similar theorem, whose proof we now sketch, holds for symmetric bounded operators in Hilbert space.

Let A be such an operator with associated bounds m, M as defined above. We establish a one-one correspondence between functions of A and real functions defined on $[m, M]$. First for polynomials: mate

$$p(A) = a_0 I + a_1 A + \cdots + a_n A^n$$

with

$$p(t) = a_0 + a_1 t + \cdots + a_n t^n,$$

I being the identity operator. This mapping is easily shown to be an algebraic isomorphism of the two algebras of polynomials. Moreover, it can be shown that $p(A)$ is positive if and only if $p(t) \geqq 0$ for every $t \in [m, M]$. Thus, $p(A) \geqq q(A)$ if and only if $p(t) \geqq q(t)$, $t \in [m, M]$.

A sequence of operators $\{A_n\}$ converges uniformly to an operator A if

$$\lim_{n \to \infty} \|A - A_n\| = 0.$$

There is another kind of convergence, called strong convergence, for operators. $\{A_n\}$ converges strongly to A if, for every $x, y \in \mathfrak{H}$,

$$\lim_{n \to \infty} (A_n x, y) = (A x, y).$$

Now, consider those real functions on $[m, M]$ which are limits of decreasing sequences of polynomials. If $\{p_n(t)\}$ converges downward to $g(t)$, then the corresponding sequence $\{p_n(A)\}$ of operators converges uniformly to an operator, symmetric and bounded, which we write as $g(A)$. This correspondence between functions and operators can be extended further, but we shall not discuss it here. Functions $e(t)$, which assume only the values 0 and 1, correspond to projection operators, since $[e(t)]^2 = e(t)$, whence $[e(A)]^2 = e(A)$. The operator A itself corresponds to the function $i(t) = t$. In the same way as $i(t)$ may be approximated by step functions, A may be approximated by sums of multiples of projections. Consider, accordingly, for every n, the partition

$$t_{n0} = m < t_{n1} = m + \frac{M - m}{n} < t_{n2}$$

$$= m + 2\frac{M - m}{n} < \cdots < t_{nn} = M.$$

Let e_u be the function which is 1 for $t \leq u$, 0 for $t > u$. Let

$$\phi_n = \sum_{k=1}^{n} t_{nk}(e_{t_{nk}} - e_{t_{nk-1}}).$$

Then $\{\phi_n\}$ converges downward to $i(t)$, so that the sequence of operators

$$A_n = \sum_{k=1}^{n} t_{nk}(e_{t_{nk}}(A) - e_{t_{nk-1}}(A))$$

converges uniformly to A. We write this as

$$A = \int_m^M \lambda \, de_\lambda = \int_{-\infty}^{\infty} \lambda \, de_\lambda.$$

Moreover, for every $x, y \in \mathfrak{H}$,

$$(Ax, y) = \int_{-\infty}^{\infty} \lambda \, d(e_\lambda x, y).$$

This is the spectral theorem for symmetric bounded operators.

THEOREM 7: *If A is a symmetric bounded operator in Hilbert space, with bounds m and M, there is a family e_λ of projections, with $e_\lambda = 0$, $\lambda < m$; $e_\lambda = I$, $\lambda \geq M$; $e_\lambda \leq e_\mu$, for $\lambda < \mu$, such that*

$$A = \int_{-\infty}^{\infty} \lambda \, de_\lambda.$$

This theorem also holds for more general bounded operators and for certain unbounded operators. It has many applications to differential and integral equations and to mathematical physics.

7. We turn to a general property of all Banach spaces, the principle of uniform boundedness. It says that if a set of bounded linear operators from a Banach space X to a Banach space Y is bounded at every $x \in X$, then it is uniformly bounded on the set $K = \{x : \|x\| = 1\}$. This is not necessarily true for normed spaces which are not complete. We prove

THEOREM 8: *If* $\mathfrak{U} = \{U\}$ *is a set of bounded linear operators on a Banach space X to a Banach space Y, then if for every $x \in X$ the set* $\{\|U(x)\| : U \in \mathfrak{U}\}$ *is bounded, it follows that the set*

$$\{\|U\| : U \in \mathfrak{U}\}$$

is bounded.

Proof: Suppose the set $\{\|U\| : U \in \mathfrak{U}\}$ is not bounded. This is the same as saying

$$\{\|U(x)\| : U \in \mathfrak{U}, \|x\| < 1\}$$

is not bounded. It follows, since $\|U(rx)\| = |r| \, \|U(x)\|$, that

$$\{\|U(x)\| : U \in \mathfrak{U}, \|x\| < r\}$$

is not bounded, for every $r > 0$. Moreover, since

$$U(x + y) = U(x) + U(y)$$

and $\{\|U(x_0)\| : U \in \mathfrak{U}\}$ is bounded for every $x_0 \in X$, it follows that

$$\{\|U(x)\| : U \in \mathfrak{U}, \|x - x_0\| < r\}$$

is unbounded, for every $x_0 \in X$, $r > 0$. We call the set

$$\{x : \|x - x_0\| < r\}$$

the open sphere $\sigma(x_0, r)$ of center x_0 and radius r, and the set

$$\{x : \|x - x_0\| \leqq r\}$$

the closed sphere $\bar{\sigma}(x_0, r)$. Thus,

(4) $$\{\|U(x)\| \,:\, U \in \mathfrak{U},\, x \in \sigma(x_0, r)\}$$

is unbounded for every open sphere $\sigma(x_0, r)$.

There are $U_1 \in \mathfrak{U}$, $x_1 \in X$, with $U_1(x_1) > 1$. By the continuity of U_1, there is a closed sphere $\bar{\sigma}(x_1, r_1)$ on which $U_1(x) > 1$. By (4), there is an

$$x_2 \in \sigma(x_1, r_1)$$

and $U_2 \in \mathfrak{U}$ such that $U_2(x_2) > 2$. By continuity of U_2, there is a closed sphere

$$\bar{\sigma}(x_2, r_2) \subset \sigma(x_1, r_1)$$

on which $U_2(x) > 2$. In this way, we obtain a nest $\{\bar{\sigma}(x_n, r_n)\}$ of closed spheres, each contained in the predecessors, and $U_n \in \mathfrak{U}$, $n = 1, 2, \cdots$, such that $U_n(x) > n$ on $\bar{\sigma}(x_n, r_n)$. Since X is complete,

$$\bigcap_{n=1}^{\infty} \bar{\sigma}(x_n, r_n)$$

is nonempty. Let

$$x_0 \in \bigcap_{n=1}^{\infty} \bar{\sigma}(x_n, r_n).$$

Then $\{U_n(x_0)\}$ is unbounded, proving the theorem.

8. A classical application of this theorem shows that the Fourier series of a continuous periodic function may diverge. Let C be the Banach space of continuous functions on $[-\pi, \pi]$ with

$$x(-\pi) = x(\pi) \quad \text{and} \quad \|x\| = \max\,\{|x(t)| \,:\, t \in [-\pi, \pi]\}.$$

For every n, let

$$s_n(x; t) = a_0 + a_1 \cos t + b_1 \sin t + \cdots + a_n \cos nt + b_n \sin nt$$

where

$$a_0 = \frac{1}{2\pi} \int_{-\pi}^{\pi} x(u)\,du, \qquad a_k = \frac{1}{\pi} \int_{-\pi}^{\pi} x(u) \cos ku\,du,$$

$$b_\kappa = \frac{1}{\pi} \int_{-\pi}^{\pi} x(u) \sin ku\,du.$$

Using an elementery identity, we obtain

$$s_n(x; t) = \frac{1}{\pi} \int_{-\pi}^{\pi} x(t + u) D_n(u) \, du$$

where
$$D_n(u) = \frac{\sin (n + \frac{1}{2}) u}{2 \sin \frac{1}{2} u}.$$

Letting $t = 0$, we obtain

$$s_n(x) = s_n(x; 0) = \frac{1}{\pi} \int_{-\pi}^{\pi} x(u) D_n(u) \, du.$$

The sequence $\{s_n(x)\}$ is the sequence of partial sums of the Fourier series of x evaluated at $t = 0$.

For every n, s_n is a linear operator on C to the one-dimensional Banach space of real numbers. It is not hard to see that s_n is continuous on C and that

$$\|s_n\| = \frac{1}{\pi} \int_{-\pi}^{\pi} |D_n(u)| \, du.$$

By means of a fairly easy calculation, it can be shown that

$$\lim_{n \to \infty} \int_{-\pi}^{\pi} |D_n(u)| \, du = \infty,$$

so that the sequence $\{\|s_n\|\}$ is unbounded. By Theorem 8, there is an $x \in C$ for which $\{s_n(x)\}$ is unbounded. In other words, there is a continuous periodic function whose Fourier series diverges at $t = 0$.

4. BANACH ALGEBRAS

1. A Banach algebra is a complex Banach space X in which, in addition to multiplication of elements in X by complex numbers, an operation xy of multiplication is defined for pairs $x, y \in X$. Multiplication will be assumed to be commutative, i.e., $xy = yx$, and to obey the rules

$$a(xy) = (ax)y = x(ay) \quad \text{and} \quad x(y + z) = xy + xz.$$

We shall assume that there is an identity e, i.e., $ex = x$. There are certain important examples where there is no identity. However, an identity can always be adjoined. Finally, we assume the norm satisfies

$$\|xy\| \leqq \|x\| \, \|y\|.$$

Some of the Banach spaces which we have discussed are also Banach algebras, in a natural choice of product. Using pointwise multiplication of functions, the space C of continuous complex-valued functions is a Banach algebra. Another example is supplied by taking the Banach space L_1, consisting of the measurable functions for which

$$\int_{-\infty}^{\infty} |f(t)| \, dt$$

is finite. Using this integral as $\|f\|$, L_1 is a Banach space; it becomes a Banach algebra if one defines a special product (*) by

$$(f*g)(x) = \int_{-\infty}^{\infty} f(t) \, g(x - t) \, dt.$$

The theory of Banach algebra was introduced by Gelfand and was largely developed by him and by Neumark, Raikov, and Shilov. Important contributions were also made by Godement, Segal, and others.

We first note that if x is such that $\|e - x\| < 1$, then x has an inverse. For,

$$\|(e - x)^n\| \leqq \|e - x\|^n,$$

so that the series $e + (e - x) + (e - x)^2 + \cdots$ converges to a $y \in X$. But

$$xy = [e - (e - x)][e + (e - x) + (e - x)^2 + \cdots] = e.$$

Now, suppose x has an inverse x^{-1}. Let U be a neighborhood of x such that

$$\sup \{\|e - zx^{-1}\| : z \in U\} < 1.$$

Then, for every $z \in U$, zx^{-1} has an inverse. Hence, the set G of points in X which have inverses is open. Moreover, the inverse is continuous on G.

2. A set $I \subset X$ is an ideal if $I \neq X$, $x, y \in I$ implies $ax + by \in I$, and $x \in X$, $y \in I$ implies $xy \in I$. If $e \in I$, then for every $x \in X$, $x = ex \in I$ so that $I = X$. This proves that e is in no ideal. The set consisting of the group identity θ is an ideal called the null ideal. If X has no ideal other than the null ideal, then X is a field. For, let $x \neq \theta$; the set

$$I = \{xy : y \in X\}$$

satisfies all conditions for an ideal except possibly $I \neq X$. It thus follows that $I = X$. Hence, there is a $y \in X$ such that $xy = e$. Therefore, X is a field.

We next note that the closure of an ideal is an ideal. This follows from the fact that an ideal cannot contain elements which have inverses. Let I be an ideal. Then $I \cap G$ is empty. Thus, the closure $\bar{I}$ of I does not meet G and $\bar{I} \neq X$. It is easy to show that $\bar{I}$ satisfies the other conditions for an ideal.

Since no ideal contains e, an easy application of Zorn's lemma shows that every ideal is contained in a maximal ideal. It also follows that maximal ideals are closed. We now prove:

x has an inverse if and only if it belongs to no maximal ideals.

Proof: If x has an inverse and is in an ideal I, then

$$xx^{-1} = e \in I,$$

which is impossible.

If x has no inverse, then the set $I = \{xy : y \in X\}$ does not contain e and so is an ideal. Hence, x is contained in a maximal ideal.

If I is an ideal, we may consider the quotient algebra X/I. If I is closed, this may be normed as a Banach algebra. Let $\xi, \eta, \cdots$ be the elements of X/I. We define

$$\|\xi\| = \inf \{\|x\| : x \in \xi\}.$$

It is obvious that $\|a\xi\| = |a| \, \|\xi\|$. Next,

$$\|\xi + \eta\| = \inf \{\|x + y\| : x \in \xi, y \in \eta\}$$
$$\leq \inf \{\|x\| + \|y\| : x \in \xi, y \in \eta\}$$
$$\leq \inf \{\|x\| : x \in \xi\} + \inf \{\|y\| : y \in \eta\}$$
$$\leq \|\xi\| + \|\eta\|,$$

and similarly,

$$\|\xi\eta\| \leq \|\xi\| \, \|\eta\|.$$

If $\xi = I$, then $\|\xi\| = 0$; conversely, suppose $\|\xi\| = 0$. Then there are $x_n \in \xi$, $n = 1, 2, \cdots$, with

$$\lim_{n \to \infty} \|x_n\| = 0.$$

Since ξ is closed, it follows that $\theta \in \xi$ so that $\xi = I$. Finally, we show that X/I is complete. Let $\{\xi_n\}$ be a Cauchy sequence. Then $\{\xi_n\}$ has a subsequence, call it $\{\xi_n\}$ also, for which

$$\sum_{n=1}^{\infty} \|\xi_{n+1} - \xi_n\| < \infty.$$

There are $x_1 \in \xi_1$, $x_2 \in \xi_2$, with

$$\|x_2 - x_1\| < 2\|\xi_2 - \xi_1\|.$$

There is $x_3 \in \xi_3$ with

$$\|x_3 - x_2\| < 2\|\xi_3 - \xi_2\|,$$

and so on. The sequence $\{x_n\}$ is Cauchy. Let $x = \lim_{n \to \infty} x_n$, and $x \in \xi$. Then $\xi = \lim_{n \to \infty} \xi_n$.

3. The following fact is basic in the study of Banach algebra.

THEOREM 9: *Every normed commutative field is isomorphic with the field of complex numbers.*

Proof: We show that every x is of the form ae. Suppose there were an $x \neq ae$ for every a. Then $(x - ae)^{-1}$ would exist for every a. By the continuity of inverse, the limit of

$$h^{-1}\{[x - (a + h)e]^{-1} - (x - ae)^{-1}\} = (x - ae - he)^{-1}(x - ae)^{-1}$$

exists and is equal to $(x - ae)^{-2}$. Hence, the function $(x - ae)^{-1}$ of the complex variable a, with values in X, has a derivative everywhere. Moreover, as a goes to infinity,

$$\|(x - ae)^{-1}\| = |a^{-1}| \left\| \left(\frac{x}{a} - e \right)^{-1} \right\|$$

goes to zero. Now, let f be any continuous linear functional on the Banach space X. It follows easily that $f((x - ae)^{-1})$ is an entire function which vanishes at infinity so that, by Liouville's theorem, $f((x - ae)^{-1})$ is identically zero. But, in a Banach space X, for every $x \neq \theta$, there is a continuous linear functional f for which $f(x) \neq 0$. (This is a nontrivial fact, but the proof will be omitted. Indeed, it is a form of the celebrated Hahn-Banach theorem.) It now follows that $(x - ae)^{-1} = \theta$, which is impossible.

4. Theorem 9 is used in conjunction with the algebraic fact that if R is a ring and M is a maximal ideal in R, then R/M is a field. We thus obtain the basic fact that in a Banach algebra X, the quotient fields, X/M, of X modulo maximal ideals M, are all isomorphic to the complex numbers.

This fact allows us to associate a function $\hat{x} = \hat{x}(M)$ on the set $\mathfrak{M}$ of maximal ideals M with every $x \in X$. Here, $\hat{x}(M)$ is the mate of the residue class modulo M to which x belongs under the isomorphism between X/M and the complex numbers. Under this mapping, θ is taken into the function $\hat{\theta}$ which is identically zero on $\mathfrak{M}$. In general, there are $x \neq \theta$ for which $\hat{x}$ is identically zero. However, if the ring X is semisimple, i.e., the intersection of the maximal ideals in X consists of θ alone, then the mapping $x \longrightarrow \hat{x}$ is one-one.

This mapping has the following properties: if $x = x_1 + x_2$ then $\hat{x} = \hat{x}_1 + \hat{x}_2$; if $x = x_1 x_2$ then $\hat{x} = \hat{x}_1 \hat{x}_2$, and $e \longrightarrow \hat{e}$ where $\hat{e}(M) = 1$ for every M. Moreover, we note that $|\hat{x}(M)| \leqq \|x\|$ for every M, since

$$|\hat{x}(M)| = \|\xi\| = \inf \{ \|y\| : y \in \xi \},$$

where ξ is the equivalence class modulo M to which x belongs.

5. We are now ready to give a proof of a theorem of Wiener as an application. Let X be the set of complex functions of a real variable

$$x(t) = \sum_{n=-\infty}^{\infty} a_n e^{int}$$

for which

$$\sum_{n=-\infty}^{\infty} |a_n| < \infty.$$

Then X is an algebra with addition and multiplication defined as usual for functions. With the norm

$$\|x\| = \sum_{n=-\infty}^{\infty} |a_n|,$$

X is easily seen to be a Banach algebra.

THEOREM 10: *If $x \in X$ is never zero then $x^{-1} \in X$.*

Proof: Let M be a maximal ideal in X. For $x = e^{it}$, let $\hat{x}(M) = a$. Then

$$|a| \leq \|e^{it}\| = 1.$$

For $x = e^{-it}$, then $\hat{x}(M) = a^{-1}$, so that

$$|a^{-1}| \leq \|e^{-it}\| = 1.$$

Hence, $|a| = 1$. Let $a = e^{it_0}$. Then, for every N, if

$$x = \sum_{n=-N}^{N} a_n e^{int}$$

it follows that

$$\hat{x}(M) = \sum_{n=-N}^{N} a_n e^{int_0}.$$

It follows that every function in X is taken into its value at t_0. Hence, M consists of those functions in X which vanish at t_0. This means that the function x of the statement of the theorem is not in M. Since x belongs to no maximal ideal, it has an inverse in X.

6. The fact that Theorem 10 has such a neat proof caused a considerable stir, and this may seem strange to a nonparticipating

observer. However, Banach algebras do have deep connections
with harmonic analysis. Lack of space does not allow a development of this topic. We simply mention that if G is a locally compact topological group, the space $L_1(G)$ of summable functions
is a Banach algebra with convolution

$$f*g(t) = \int_G f(tu^{-1})g(u) \, du$$

as multiplication. This algebra has an identity if and only if G
is discrete. In the general case, an identity may be adjoined or
other devices used. The maximal ideal space has a natural
topology which turns out to be essentially the same as the dual
of G with its topology. The representation of f is the Fourier
transform of f. Plancherel's theorem is valid and is closely
related to the Pontryagin duality theorem. The theorem of
Bochner on positive definite functions and the Wiener tauberian
theorem remain valid in this setting.

5. HISTORICAL SUPPLEMENT

The idea of functional analysis was introduced by Volterra
in the 1880's in his work on integral equations. Further early
contributions were made by Hadamard, who also suggested the
name *functional analysis*. The notions of metric space and of
compactness were introduced by Frechet in the first decade of
this century. Other early investigations were those of Hilbert
on integral equations. He also made a suggestive contribution
to the Dirichlet principle. In 1923, Tonelli's book appeared, in
which the calculus of variations is approached from the viewpoint of functional analysis.

In 1918, in an important paper on integral equations, F.
Riesz introduced the axioms for complete normed vector spaces.
Several years later, Banach initiated the systematic use of these
spaces. An important technique involving their use in real and
complex function theories is credited to Saks. Since that time,
the subject has had a great development, as well as fruitful
application to function theory, differential and integral equa-

tions, and the theory of approximation. Perhaps special mention should be made of the Schauder-Leray existence theory for differential equations. A journal, *Studia Mathematica*, which flourished in the 1930's, and is again active, is largely devoted to functional analysis.

Banach himself had already considered vector spaces which cannot be normed but are metrizable. Moreover, Banach spaces are not even metrizable in their weak topologies. The idea of topological vector spaces, in which the topology is such that the vector-space operations are continuous, occurred in 1934 to Kolmogorov, who gave necessary and sufficient conditions for such a space to be normable. A year later, von Neumann gave axioms for such spaces and developed a theory. This led to further studies by other mathematicians, but the theory seemed to lack motivation. With the advent of distribution theory, which requires nonmetrizable topological vector spaces, the theory was rejuvenated. The contributions of Dieudonné and Mackey to duality theory were made even before distribution theory, and the later contributions of Bourbaki and Grothendieck are very interesting. The Bourbaki view is to focus attention on vital properties of spaces, and to determine which spaces have these properties. Distribution theory is being applied especially to the study of differential operators. Recent work of Browder, in which the point of working instead with certain types of discontinuous operators is taken, may become important.

The axioms for Hilbert space were introduced by von Neumann in 1928, and a study of certain unbounded operators was made by him, partly in connection with his work on the foundations of quantum theory. At about the same time, similar work was done by Stone; also by Wintner.

An order relation exists for functions and for certain operators, and the concept of vector lattice was first used in this connection by F. Riesz in 1928. Further early work, relating vector lattices with norms, was done by Freudenthal and by Kantorovitch. Nakano has made important contributions. This whole subject has only been developed in part. The work of Köthe on spaces of sequences has some relation to this topic. The work on

Banach algebras, especially those centering on the Wiener tauberian theorem, and the papers of von Neumann and Murray on rings of operators, and the many subsequent generalizations, deserve mention.

BIBLIOGRAPHY

BOOKS

1. Aronszajn, N., *Introduction to the Theory of Hilbert Space*. Stillwater, Okla.: Oklahoma Research Foundation, 1950.

2. Banach, S., *Théorie des operations linéaires*. Warsaw: Monografie Matematyczne, 1932.

3. Goffman, C., *Linear Spaces*, Purdue Lecture Notes in Mathematics, Lafayette, Indiana: Purdue University.

4. Halperin, I., *Introduction to the Theory of Distributions*. Toronto: University of Toronto Press, 1952.

5. Hilbert, D., *Grundzüge einer allgemeine Theorie der linearen Integralgleichungen*. Leipzig: B. G. Teubner, 1912.

6. Kolmogorov, A. N. and S. V. Fomin, *Metric and Normed Spaces*. Volume 1 of *Elements of the Theory of Functions and Functional Analysis* (English trans.). Rochester: Graylock Press, 1957.

7. Lighthill, M. J., *Introduction to Fourier Integrals and Generalized Functions*. Cambridge: Cambridge University Press, 1958.

8. Ljusternik, L. A. and W. I. Sobolew, *Elemente der Funktionalanalysis* (German trans.). Berlin: Berlin Akademie, 1955.

9. Loomis, L. H., *An Introduction to Abstract Harmonic Analysis*. New York: Van Nostrand Co., 1953.

10. Montel, P. A., *Leçons sur les familles normales des fonctions et leurs applications*. Paris: Gauthier-Villars et Cie, 1927.

11. Riesz, F. and B. St.-Nagy, *Leçons d'analyse fonctionelle*, 3rd ed. Budapest: Akademiai Kiado, 1955.

12. Stone, M. H., *Linear Transformations in Hilbert Space and Their Applications to Analysis*. New York: American Mathematical Society, 1932.

13. Taylor, A. E., *Introduction to Functional Analysis.* New York: John Wiley Co., 1958.

14. von Neumann, J., *Mathematical Foundations of Quantum Theory* (English trans.). Princeton: Princeton University Press, 1955.

15. Wintner, A., *Spectraltheorie der Unendlichen Matrizen.* Leipzig: S. Hirzel, 1929.

16. Zaanen, A. C., *Linear Analysis.* Amsterdam: North-Holland Publishing Co., 1953.

PAPERS REFERRED TO IN TEXT

1. Banach, S. and H. Steinhaus, "Sur le principe de la condensation de singularités," *Fundamenta Mathematicae,* Vol. 9 (1927), pp. 51–57.

2. Bourbaki, N., "Sur certain espaces vectoriels topologiques," *Annales de l'Institut Fourier,* Vol. 2 (1951), pp. 5–16.

3. Browder, F. E., "Functional analysis and partial differential equations, I," *Mathematische Annalen,* Vol. 138 (1959), pp. 55–79.

4. Dieudonné, J., "La dualité dans les espaces vectoriels topologiques," *Annales scientifiques de l'École Normale Supérieure,* ser. 3, Vol. 59 (1942), pp. 107–39.

5. Dieudonné, J. and L. Schwartz, "La dualité dans les espaces (F) et (LF)," *Annales de l'Institut Fourier,* Vol. 1 (1950), pp. 61–101.

6. Fréchet, M., "Sur quelques points du calcul fonctionnel," *Rendiconti del Circolo Matematico di Palermo,* t. 22 (1906), pp. 1–71.

7. Freudenthal, H., "Teilweise geordnete moduln," *Koninklijke Nederlandse Akademie Van Wetenschappen* (Amsterdam), Vol. 39 (1936), pp. 641–51.

8. Gelfand, I., "Normierte ringe," *Matematiceskii Sbornik,* N.S. 9, (1941), pp. 3–23.

9. Gelfand, I. and G. Shilov, "Fourier transforms of rapidly increasing functions and questions of uniqueness of the solution of Cauchy's problem," *American Mathematical Society Translation,* ser. 2, Vol. 5 (1957), pp. 221–74.

10. Grothendieck, A., "Produit tensoriels topologiques et espaces nucleaires," *Memoirs of the American Mathematical Society,* ser. 2, Vol. 5 (1957), pp. 221–74.

11. Hadamard, J., "Sur les operations fonctionnelles," *Comptes rendus de l'Académie des Sciences*, Paris (1903), pp. 351–54.

12. Hilbert, D., "Sur le principe de Dirichlet," *Nouvelle Annales de Mathématiques*, ser. 3, t. 19 (1900), pp. 337–44.

13. Kantorovitch, L. V., "Linear operations in semiordered spaces," *Matematiceskii Sbornik*, N.S. 2, (1937), pp. 121–65.

14. Kolmogorov, A. N., "Zur normierbarkeit eines allgemeinen topologischen linearen Raumes," *Studia mathematica*, Vol. 5 (1935), pp. 29–33.

15. Köthe, G., "Neubegrundung der Theorie der vollkommenen Raume," *Mathematische Nachrichten*, Vol. 4 (1951), pp. 70–80.

16. Leray, J. and J. Schauder, "Topologie et équations fonctionelles," *Annales scientifiques de l'École Normale Supérieure*, ser. 3, Vol. 51 (1934), pp. 45–78.

17. Mackey, G. W., "On convex topological linear spaces," *Transactions of the American Mathematical Society*, Vol. 60 (1946), pp. 519–37.

18. Murray, F. J. and J. von Neumann, "On rings of operators," *Annals of Mathematics*, Vol. 37 (1936), pp. 116–229.

19. Riesz, F., "Sur la décomposition des operations fonctionelles linéaires," *International Congress of Mathematics* (Bologna), Vol. 3 (1928), pp. 143–48.

20. Riesz, F., "Über lineare funktionalgleichungen," *Acta mathematica*, Vol. 41 (1917), pp. 71–98.

21. Volterra, V., "Sopra le funzioni che dipendono da altre funzioni," *Atti della Academia Nazionale dei Lincei*, Vol. 6 (1887).

22. von Neumann, J., "Allgemeine eigenwerttheorie Hermitescher funktionaloperatoren," *Mathematische Annalen*, Vol. 102 (1929), pp. 49–131.

23. von Neumann, J., "On complete topological spaces," *Transactions of the American Mathematical Society*, Vol. 37 (1935), pp. 1–20.

INDEX